All Rachel could see was that this man had interfered with her life, determinedly, ruthlessly, and with a speed that even now left her feeling that it must be unreal. This was not a man who allowed such foolish things as convention and decent behaviour to stand in his path.

She felt a rising triumph of her own. She had a stick with which to beat the devil and she would use it unmercifully. Nick Orsiani would remember the name Rachel Gordon, long after he had forgotten any other woman.

'You will come with me to Rome, Rachel?' he asked softly.

'Yes.'

Then he laughed, a low murmur of amusement and, rather frighteningly, a sound of delight.

'You will play a dangerous game with me, *signorina*?' he enquired softly. 'You will play it on my territory with my rules? Do not forget that only one can win and that the winner takes all. I am willing to play your game. The prize could become an obsession!'

A MOMENT OF ANGER

BY
PATRICIA WILSON

MILLS & BOON LIMITED
ETON HOUSE   18-24 PARADISE ROAD
RICHMOND   SURREY   TW9 1SR

*First published in Great Britain 1987
by Mills & Boon Limited*

© Patricia Wilson 1987

*Australian copyright 1987
Philippine copyright 1987
This edition 1987*

ISBN 0 263 75797 8

*Set in Plantin 10 on 10½ pt.
01-1087-54489*

*Computer typeset by SB Datagraphics,
Colchester, Essex*

*Printed and bound in Great Britain by
Collins, Glasgow*

CHAPTER ONE

'I DON'T much like the idea of being overtaken,' Cynthia remarked worriedly, perching on the edge of Rachel's desk, her eyes on the nail she was re-varnishing carefully. 'I mean, it's really frightening when you come to think of it.'

Rachel Gordon's deep brown eyes looked up in amusement as her slender fingers stopped their skilled and rapid movements, remaining poised over the keys of the typewriter.

'I can see that it would be,' she laughed. 'But the expression you're looking for is "taken over". The firm was taken over two years ago. You certainly frighten slowly.' She turned back to her work but Cynthia hadn't finished yet.

'Yes, but there's bound to be a big shake-up now, isn't there? Otherwise the big boss man himself wouldn't be arriving after lunch.'

'There's not much doubt that you will be very well shaken up if you don't get back to the switchboard,' Rachel asserted, glancing anxiously at her watch, needing to have her office to herself and get on with her work. 'Besides, you're worrying about nothing. If you didn't spend half your day listening in to private conversations you wouldn't be nearly so anxious. You know the old saying, a listener never hears any good of himself.' She nodded towards the door, indicating the way out.

'What do you know, Rachel?' Cynthia pleaded, screwing the top back on to her nail varnish, reluctant to leave, every movement slow.

'I'm a private secretary. Notice the word private,' Rachel said firmly. 'If I knew anything I wouldn't tell you, but honestly, I've no idea why Signor Orsiani is coming.'

'They say he's got more women than an Arab sheikh,' Cynthia confided in a blood-curdling whisper, another excuse to linger. 'They say he goes from one to the other—fast!'

'Which goes to show how little they know!' Rachel answered pertly, going back determinedly to her work. 'I met him two years ago. He's small, plump, bald-headed and fatherly, sixty-five if he's a day. Now will you go? I've got to get these letters out by lunch time. I expect I'll have to take notes at the meeting and I don't know yet whether they're going to use the boardroom or the office. I don't even know whether Signor Orsiani is coming alone or with a party. Just go back to the switchboard and stop worrying.'

'It's all right for you,' Cynthia complained as she finally reached the door of Rachel's office. 'You're leaving to get married. Whatever happens, it's not going to affect you.'

'Whether you get overtaken or shaken up, you're going to survive,' Rachel said with a patience that amazed her, 'unless you decide to stay here and stop me from getting on, of course!'

One look into Rachel's eyes and Cynthia left quickly, seeing the danger signals. Rachel got down to work, shaking her head in disbelief. What other rumours were circulating? she wondered. No doubt Chris would have a few to tell her when she met him for dinner tonight. The thought spurred her on. If she didn't finish these she was likely to find herself working late tonight, because certainly the afternoon would be taken up with the meeting—and several more days, too, she suspected, before they could all breathe more easily. She knew that her boss was worried; Cynthia was not the only one.

She must admit, although she wouldn't have dreamed of admitting it to Cynthia, that the thought of the meeting was a little bit alarming. Apart from the fact that Bill Taylor, her boss, was forty-two, with a wife, two children and a mortgage to support, there was the question of Chris's job. When they got married she was going to stop working. She didn't particularly want to do that, but Chris was insistent. But if Chris lost his job, or if she tried to stay and lost hers ... She snapped herself out of this foolish speculation, giving a little mutter of irritation as she found that she had typed one word three times. This sort of thing was going to get her nowhere.

Anyway, Chris was ambitious, a go-getter; there was no doubt about it, nobody was going to move him from the firm. Since the take-over, he was the only pilot they had and somebody had to fly the helicopters. But still ... She pulled herself back to the job in hand, putting everything else firmly from her mind, but she couldn't prevent her eyes from wandering worriedly over to the corner of her office where files were stacked knee deep in readiness on the floor. Signor Orsiani had asked for all the files. He hadn't done that when he had been here two years ago when the take-over of Fenland Helicopters was new, and the powerful Orsiani Italia had devoured the small family firm, incorporating it with the huge Italian company without a blink or a sign of financial indigestion. Something was definitely going to happen, and she only hoped that whatever it was it would not affect her or the people she cared about. She had been too happy here for far too long to dismiss the problems of the rest of the staff with an easy shrug. They may now all be part of the giant Orsiani Italia, but there was still a family atmosphere in the place.

After Cynthia's lengthy interruption and interruptions from various other people who were beginning to get themselves into a state of panic about their future in the firm, Rachel found that she was only just finishing the mail at lunchtime.

During the course of the morning, Bill Taylor had gone out and she sincerely hoped that he would be back in time to greet the Italian or the Italian party; she didn't much fancy the idea of having to see to them herself. Normally she wouldn't have been particularly bothered—she was accustomed to taking responsibility—but the state of feverish panic that was beginning to spread through the offices and the works, much of it centred on her, everybody being sure that she knew more than she did, was having an effect on her, even though she knew that whatever happened it was unlikely to touch her personally.

Even Margaret Taylor, Bill's wife, had been on the phone, talking for ages, convinced that Bill was keeping some really bad news from her and trying to wheedle out of Rachel facts that Rachel could not produce, and Rachel knew that her lunch hour was going to be a sort of race against the clock.

She managed to snatch a quick lunch in town, though, calling into the bank in the slack lunch-hour period to pay some more money into the joint account that she and Chris had ready for their wedding, walking back to the office with easy swinging steps, her mind more calm. Getting away from the office had proved to be a very good thing because, when she came back in, the little flutter that had been growing inside her had calmed down. Panic was certainly infectious, she thought with a wry smile.

There was utter silence from Bill's office and she wondered if the Italians had arrived during her break and if Bill had taken them out for a meal. She hoped so, because she could do with a few more minutes of peace and quiet. Being flustered was not her style, and she wasn't quite sure which files would be needed first.

It occurred to her that Bill might have left a note for her on his desk; he often did. She tidied her long auburn hair in the mirror, removing the jacket of her dark green suit, straightening the cream silk blouse and looking at herself critically.

She was tall, slim, sometimes she thought a little too thin, but Chris liked her slender figure, although her mother was constantly urging her to try and gain a little more weight. Not that many people studied her shape, she thought with a wry grin. They were always too startled by the heavy, bright hair that fell in soft waves around her small, delicate face. The hair was the same colour as her father's, her mother had told her, but she pushed the thought away from her now with more ease than she had been able to do when she was a child. Her mother's bitterness was rarely mentioned now, and it was too far removed from Rachel for her to let it colour her own life.

Walking across to Bill's office, going in without knocking as the room was so obviously empty, she turned to the desk, her mind elsewhere, half of it on the afternoon meeting, half of it mentally adding up and working out what she and Chris would do with the money in the joint account.

The office wasn't empty! There was a man sitting beside Bill's desk, his chair pulled sideways, his long, strong legs stretched out in front of him. They were the first things she saw, dark clad and elegantly crossed. His eyes met her startled gaze as she came to a sudden halt and looked up.

Even though he was sitting down, she could see that he was very tall, his hair black as jet, his skin darkly tanned, olive-tinted. But most astonishingly, his eyes were grey, light grey, so clear as to be almost silver; they seemed to dominate his face. A fierce feeling hit her somewhere deep inside, almost painful, every nerve-ending she had beginning to tingle with uneasy life.

He stretched slowly to his full height. He was immaculately dressed, his dark suit fitting his powerful frame to perfection, the crisp white shirt a startling contrast against his dark skin. She seemed to be noticing everything about him in the flash of a second as if the world had started to spin more slowly, an odd, alarming feeling that left her breathless and with a feeling of growing panic as she stood there like a film frozen in the frame.

She didn't even try to speak because she was quite sure that she would never manage it, and he wasn't speaking either; he was just standing there looking comfortably at ease, remarkably different from the way she was feeling. Nobody had ever stopped her in her tracks before like this and she was quivering inside, a strange pulsing feeling running through her that kept her eyes fixed on his.

All the fine hairs on her skin were suddenly standing upright in a primeval signal of danger and the silence was so intense that if anyone had walked in she knew she would have given a little scream of shock because she felt completely hypnotised, as if she were waiting for orders with a sort of vibrating disquiet inside her that was growing by the second. She recognised her body's alarm reactions but there was nothing she could do but stand there staring.

Rachel felt, rather than saw, his eyes move, his glance running over her from head to foot before coming back to linger on the rich red-gold of her hair. He allowed his gaze to move over the creamy skin of her face, to the quick rise and fall of her breasts beneath the cream silk blouse, and she felt a swift and further rise in her alarm as her breasts seemed to surge and swell, the nipples hardening against the thin material. Silent shame flooded through her as even in her dazed state she realised that he had noticed, his eyes coming back to hers for a second before wandering down the slender length of her body.

Every bit of her skin began to tingle as he looked at her, burning wherever his eyes moved as if he had touched her quivering flesh with his fingertips, silently exploring every inch of her.

She had never felt like this before in her life, standing there like a puppet that was slowly being given an existence, feeling that she was waiting for the order to move, as if he had every right to act like this.

Deep inside, she knew that the way he was looking at her was wrong, unthinkable, that she should be walking out, right out of the building, calling for help. He seemed to be removing every garment that she wore one at a time, without any seductive gaze but with a deliberate pace as if she was a slender statue that he was unveiling, taking his time, the better to enjoy the full viewing. She could feel the blood rush into her face, pounding in her ears as his eyes moved back to hers, his face as cool and still as it had been all the time.

'I expect that you are Miss Gordon?' She almost jumped out of her skin at the sound of his voice, her scrambled mind hastily grasping the fact that there was a trace of accent on some of the words, trying to feel relieved that he might be one of the Italian party and praying desperately that he wasn't.

'Signor Taylor will be back in a moment,' he continued as she made no attempt to answer, the effort being beyond her at that moment as the grey eyes bored into hers. 'Can I help you?' he added quietly.

This was crazy, she told herself. This was Bill's office. He had just used the words that she should have been using, as if she was the visitor, she thought rather wildly. He must think she was some sort of imbecile, standing there, saying nothing, not moving. No wonder he was staring at her so coolly; maybe he was thinking of ringing for someone to take her away and lock her up!

'Does—does he know that you're here?'

She had to try to recover from this, to find out who he was and get him out of there, because at any moment Bill would surely be back with Signor Orsiani and if this man wasn't one of the expected visitors then she would have some explaining to do.

'He knows that I am here.' He said nothing more, seemingly totally taken up with watching her, his eyes beginning to move over her again with the same slow investigation that was churning her up inside.

'I don't know if you have an appointment,' she said hurriedly, her face feeling fiery, 'but Mr Taylor is going to be very busy this afternoon. Mr Orsiani is coming and ...'

'I am Orsiani.'

He said it with no inflexion, almost vaguely, never looking up, still intent on his slow inspection of her, his eyes on the slim outlines of her body, the slender length of her legs.

His announcement snapped her out of her odd daze, however, although it did nothing to remove her embarrassment or the rapid palpitations of her heart.

'No. No, you're not! I know Mr Orsiani. He's an old gentleman, he's ...'

'My father. Having retired, he will not be here. I run Orsiani Italia.' His eyes flashed up from her figure to meet hers with cool, keen certainty, locking with her own, holding her wide, dark-eyed gaze.

'Oh! I'm sorry—— I mean—he was nice ...'

'He still is. He is not dead, merely retired. He has a way with people,' he added slowly, unsmiling, his eyes beginning to inspect her every feature separately. 'Let us hope, Miss Gordon, that everyone finds me equally nice.'

He didn't seem to imagine that everyone would find him equally nice and clearly he didn't care: his voice was utterly offhand and there was something about the way that he said it that clouded her mind with worry again. She realised that anyone who had seen him arrive was now going to be in a state of even greater panic because he didn't look much like a man who would compromise in anything. If he had come to shake them up, they would be well shaken.

'Can—can I get you a cup of coffee while you wait?' she asked rather desperately. She was doing everything she could to push herself back into her normal role, to fight off the awesome feeling that she had stepped into a dream that she hadn't dreamed herself, somebody else's dream. It wasn't actually a nightmare but it was close enough to it, as if she couldn't quite shake off a bad night.

His hands were in his pockets now, his jacket pushed back. He looked wealthy, calm, completely at ease, but she was still in a state of trembling agitation and she was quite sure that he had noticed that all right. His eyes now never left her flustered face as if her stupidity fascinated him; there was even a faint look of wonder on his face as if he couldn't quite believe that anyone could be so inept and still be allowed to wander around alone.

She really ought to be dealing with him firmly, efficiently, but somehow he had the reins, even in an unfamiliar óffice, and he was leaving her in no doubt that he was Orsiani while she was a small cog in the wheels of a mighty firm, a mere secretary.

If he would sit down, turn round, pick up a pencil, do something other than stare at her, she might be able to get her act together, but she realised that he wasn't going to sit down until she had left the room. His courtesy was obviously very strong—unless he enjoyed dominating people with his height; it was a distinct possibility!

'A cup of coffee?' He looked doubtful. 'Forgive me if I offend you, but I have found English coffee to be—peculiar. It is to be made in one of those—machines?'

Without warning, he seemed almost human and she laughed in relief, her small, perfect teeth showing against the coral of her lips.

'No. I have all the necessary things in my office. I'll make it myself.' She had relaxed just for a second and she nearly saw a smile on his lips, but it didn't quite make it. He was like good-quality marble; certainly he was expensive.

'Thank you. If you are to make it then I would certainly like some.'

'I—I'll just be a minute.'

Suddenly, ridiculously, idiotically, she didn't know how to get out of the room, and for the first time cool amusement seemed to come to the back of his eyes as he appeared to recognise her predicament. She backed away, feeling for the door behind her, beginning to get more than a little annoyed with this cold-faced man.

'I won't be long.' She stepped through the door and closed it a little too quickly; it almost sounded as if she had slammed it. She realised that she had been holding her breath for the last few minutes, a panic racing inside her very close to the surface. Her breath came out in a great shuddering sigh as she closed her eyes, leaning against the door, her legs shaking, her heart racing. She was almost hysterically glad to have the door between them. She wasn't quite sure what had happened in there, but something had. Nobody, but nobody had ever looked at her like that before. He had undressed her with his eyes and then put her back together again and she was still tingling as if it had really happened, her breath

coming in shallow gasps now that she had let her feeble
amount of control slip. She could still hear his voice, 'I
am Orsiani.' Even the way he said it was daunting, as if
he needed no trimmings, no polite titles, as if his name
and personality alone were enough.

Well, they were enough for her. She felt almost close
to frightened tears and her hands were still trembling as
she made the coffee. Her control had never slipped
before in the whole of her adult life but it had wobbled
perilously close there, and she could have wept with
relief as Bill Taylor came striding into the office, grim-
faced.

'Coffee? Good! I need it!'

He looked ruffled and normally Rachel would have
smiled secretly at the sign of his petulance. He didn't like
his calm world to be disturbed, and she had often agreed
with Margaret Taylor that Bill could be thoroughly
childish when things were not going his way. In his
wife's opinion, part of Rachel's job was to smooth his
way through a day at the office as Margaret smoothed
his life at home, and she agreed.

Today, though, she felt as if she hadn't a smile in her,
and she watched him walk to his office with nothing but
deep sympathy. He was a little overweight, a little too
spoiled by Margaret at home and Rachel at work, a little
too comfortable. There was no comfort waiting for him
today though. The Iceman had come and it wasn't a jolly
snowman sitting in there. He was too much for Bill; too
much for anyone, she suspected.

She took a deep breath and lifted the tray, straightening her back and composing her face, pretending really
hard that she couldn't care less who was in Bill's office,
her fiery head raised proudly as she walked into the other
room.

This time, the Italian didn't get to his feet. He leaned
back in his chair, watching indolently as she placed the

tray on a table near to Bill's desk and began to pour the coffee. Some of the taut, cold look about him seemed to have gone, but he still looked dangerous, the most dangerous man she had ever seen.

'You may as well be the first to know, Rachel,' Bill suddenly burst out, fiendishly petulant. 'I'm being moved to Rome!'

'Rome!' Her head shot up and this time, she knew, her mouth was open, her startled eyes flashing to the Italian and back to Bill.

'Exactly! If I didn't tell you now, I knew that Margaret would be on the phone as soon as I got back home and told her. She'll probably be delighted,' he added in disgust, slumping into his chair.

Rachel wasn't quite sure what she was expected to say but she never got the chance, as it happened.

'An Italian manager will replace Signor Taylor here for six months,' the cool-eyed Italian informed her, obviously thinking that as she knew one thing she may as well know the rest, although it was clear that he thought it to be none of her business. 'There is to be a greater integration in the future; it is good for the firm. I would like, for example, every person in a position of authority to speak both languages with some degree of fluency; the move will facilitate this. The Italian manager will bring his own secretary and several members of his staff so that at least he will have some people around him who are familiar. We do not wish to rock the firm too wildly. Signor Taylor will do the same. You will like Rome, *signorina*,' he finished smoothly. 'It can be an exciting city.'

He was still leaning back, watching her coolly, waiting no doubt, she thought with a flare of annoyance, for her to say, 'Oh goody!' and hug him in gratitude, or possibly he wanted her to lick his expensive suede shoes.

'Rachel won't be going to Rome, Mr Orsiani. It was

bad enough knowing that I was going to lose her and still be here. God knows how I'll cope without her in Rome!' He sighed loudly and Rachel looked at him in horror, trying to warn him to keep quiet just this once. As far as she could see, he was talking himself right out of a job, straight into the ranks of the unemployed. There was nothing about the Italian that led her to believe that he would lean across and say, 'There, there,' in a consoling manner. He was more likely to say, 'If you can't cope, get out,' and she saw his face tighten with quick anger.

She was the one, however, who took the brunt of his displeasure.

'Losing her? You are leaving the firm, Miss Gordon? I would very much like to know why. If you have been offered a higher salary, we will top it! We do not like to lose valuable employees, and besides, as private secretary to the manager, you must certainly have a wide knowledge of the firm's affairs. We do not like our new ideas to be spread widely afield. Industry is extremely competitive in the modern world!'

Rachel's lips opened in astonishment at this insult and then clamped together in one straight line and the brown eyes that met the cold silver of the Italian's were furious, blazing at him, wide open.

'Mr Orsiani ...' she began, but Bill intervened.

'Rachel! Now, Rachel!' He glanced at the Italian as if he had gone secretly and suicidally mad. 'Rachel is hardly likely to spread anything afield,' he growled protectively, glancing at her warily from the corner of his eye. 'She's utterly reliable. And I don't know, Mr Orsiani, if you have any Italian women with red hair but we tend to watch our step in England with somebody of Rachel's colouring.' He looked as if he was considering standing in between them; clearly he had not given a thought to his own job, speaking like this to the big man. Rachel's mouth was clamped shut again but, if the

Italian said anything to Bill, she would wade right in there.

'Anyway,' Bill added with a return to self-pity, 'she's not going to another job, she's leaving to get married. Two months away now, isn't it, Rachel?'

She nodded curtly, turning back to the coffee tray, her annoyance by no means under control. She poured Bill's coffee and placed it on his desk, seriously contemplating pouring Signor Orsiani's on to his lap, her eyes still bright with anger.

'I see.' He knew how she felt; he seemed to be daring her to scald him with hot coffee and his own annoyance was still in his voice. 'Perhaps you could postpone your wedding and fly to Rome with Signor Taylor and assist him? He will need you and there is very little difference between two months and six months.'

He wasn't about to apologise then for treating her like an industrial spy! No wonder her hair had nearly stood on end. The wolf had come to gobble them up! Well, he could just sit there and snap his teeth!

'The difference, Mr Orsiani, is four months exactly!' she said with a coldness to match his. 'I could not postpone my wedding.'

'Not even out of loyalty to your immediate boss?' he enquired scathingly. 'I seem to have gained the impression that Signor Taylor's wife is a friend. She will welcome a person she knows in Italy, a friendly face. Of course your salary will rise, too.'

Rachel's face was not at all friendly as she looked straight at him. She had the advantage. He was still seated and she was tall herself, very regal at the moment, her creamy face stiff with annoyance.

'I think, Mr Orsiani, that my fiancé has first claim on my loyalty. My resignation is not yet on Mr Taylor's desk, but as you can see, he knows that I leave in just under two months. I am only required to give one month's notice.'

'Look, I'm sorry I started all this,' Bill interrupted contritely, puzzled by the animosity his remarks had engendered. Normally he could grumble with no fear of retaliation, but now he felt as if the air was on fire. They were like two angry cats, circling each other. 'Chris wouldn't take kindly to any postponement. He's the helicopter pilot with the firm. You'll see his file,' he added hopefully to the Italian, trying to restore order by introducing a third party.

If he had been hoping for a gleaming smile, a friendly word, an interested comment, he was certainly disappointed.

'Perhaps we could get on with the files?' the Italian rasped, and Bill nodded miserably, glancing at Rachel without hope.

'Will you want me to take notes, Mr Taylor?' she asked, willing him to say no.

He met her eyes and decided to be grown up for once.

'Er—no, Rachel. I think . . .'

'Yes!' the cool voice intervened. 'There is much to do. Your note-taking will speed up the process.' The power had spoken and Bill shrugged resignedly, looking quite guilty at the trouble his grumbles had caused, but Rachel wasn't blaming him.

'About the rest of the party, Mr Taylor. Are they . . .'

'I am the party, Miss Gordon, all of it! If you could bring in the first of the files please?'

He met her eyes coldly; he was still annoyed. Well, so was she: furious! He certainly was the party, the nastiest party she'd ever met, the most arrogant, the most ruthless, the most selfish . . .

'The files, Miss Gordon?'

He was looking at her with raised eyebrows, looking as if he could read her mind, and she hoped he could. She met his scowl with a good one of her own, wanting to walk across and push his chair off balance, him in it.

'Yes, sir!' She walked out with a straight back, well aware that angry eyes were boring into her back, feeling smugly immune. She was leaving, thank goodness. A spell in Italy with the chance of seeing him frequently would possibly lead to her being arrested for criminal assault.

She hardly had time to breathe during the rest of the afternoon and her annoyance quickly changed to alarm again long before three-thirty came around.

She had known the people whose files were being methodically invaded and dissected for over five years, since she had joined the firm when she was eighteen, but the cold-faced Italian seemed to know as much about them as she did after a few minutes with each file, working through them with total concentration as if he was alone in the room.

His grasp of things was actually frightening and his speed of reading left her numb. An odd remark to Bill, a deeply loaded question, and she found herself wincing as the characters she knew so well unfolded before his cool, grey eyes like so many paper cut-outs, every fault disclosed in spite of Bill's hedging.

She found herself staring helplessly at the dark head bent over the files, and once she was so mesmerised that she missed the beginning of the dictation, unaware that he was speaking until his glance flashed up to her fascinated face and he snapped long brown fingers.

'Miss Gordon?'

'Sorry, sir.' She dipped her bright head and her pencil tore along. He expected a speed that had her imagining that before long the page would begin to smoulder, set fire to her skirt. She giggled with a bubbly feeling of frightened hysteria but he stopped that rapidly.

'Miss Gordon? We are, I hope on the same

wavelength? I do not recall introducing a note of
humour. Please read back the last paragraph!'

She did, and dared not look up again. Bill would
probably be up all night with his nerves; he was sitting
stunned now until spoken to.

'Who is next?'

'Er—it's Chris. Chris Pearson.' Bill looked apologet-
ically at Rachel but the Italian tossed the file aside as she
handed it across.

'He is the helicopter pilot, you said? Then as he is in a
category of his own, I will deal with him separately.'

He glanced at his expensive watch and suddenly
looked across at Rachel, no animosity on his face
whatever, his grey eyes holding her startled gaze
steadily.

'Is it not true that in England everything stops for
tea?' She gaped a little, feeling herself falling backwards
into idiocy and he smiled widely, a flash of brilliantly
white teeth against the tanned face. 'It is almost four.
Perhaps we could take the traditional break and then you
can type the notes, Miss Gordon, while Signor Taylor
and I wander around the works. We will all relax, yes?'

'Yes, sir.' She stood stiffly and made a dignified
retreat.

Yes, Mr Orsiani. No, Mr Orsiani. Oh, thank you, Mr
Orsiani! An afternoon with him had reduced her to a
state of shock. She felt more like a new tea-boy than a
private secretary. Not that being a private secretary was
anything; she felt somehow that that fact had been
impressed on her silently this afternoon. Wait until
Chris heard all this! She looked at her watch as the kettle
began to boil. One and a half hours to go. When the
works' siren went she was going to be the first out, even
if she had to climb over Signor Orsiani in the scramble.
It had definitely been the longest day of her life. If she
had kept a diary she would have torn the page out. He

had lowered her to the ranks of the insignificant and barely coherent.

She took the tray of tea in and beat a hasty retreat, ignoring Bill's pleading eyes. He was just going to have to cope alone because she had enough notes to fill a crate, it seemed, and the Italian would probably gulp down his tea, walk in and ask if she'd finished.

He didn't, though, and she kept her head bent over her work, her slender fingers flying over the typewriter keys as she heard Bill's office door open and they both walked through.

'You'll be gone by the time we get back,' Bill said plaintively as if he hoped that she'd sit up all night and help to calm him. ''Night, Rachel.'

'Goodnight, Mr Taylor.' She never stopped and with a sigh of relief she heard the outer door close. He'd gone. Hurrah! She looked up to relish her happiness.

He hadn't! He was standing in the open doorway, watching her, his silvery eyes sardonically intent on her face.

'Goodnight, Miss Gordon.'

'Good-goodnight, sir.'

Her face flushed at the quirk of amusement at the edge of the cool lips, at the arrogant gravity of his farewell nod, and then he had closed the door quietly, as quietly as he had re-opened it. Even at the last minute he had reduced her to a mindless jellyfish. She glared at the typewriter and typed 'Damn! Damn! Damn!' before tearing the sheet out and tossing it into the wastepaper basket. She could have typed more, but propriety forbade it and anyway, somebody would collect the waste.

She hadn't finished the typing when the works' siren blew but she left anyway. Tomorrow was tomorrow and she would face it when it arrived; today had been more than enough and she still felt uneasy.

'Didn't I tell you that he had more women than an Arab sheikh?' Cynthia called as Rachel passed the switchboard. 'Isn't he beautiful? He's so ...'

'I know what he is, thank you,' Rachel said stonily. She did! He was abominable, utterly unfeeling, indescribable. 'There is very little difference between two months and six months.' Imagine! He had actually expected her to postpone her wedding to accommodate Orsiani Italia!

He would probably be found to have been made out of spare bits of metal left over from the production line if anyone ever cared to inspect him closely. The thought turned her mind to a subject she had kept well away from. He had inspected her closely.

She felt a sudden and unwelcome tingle as she remembered how the glittering grey eyes had wandered all over her, inspecting every inch of her, the stab of queer pain inside returning sharply as she remembered. It was probably because he was an Italian, she told herself swiftly; she'd heard about them. But she could still feel his eyes on her, even in the crowded bus, and she flushed with embarrassment and alarm at the feeling, still very much present, that this afternoon she had been slowly undressed and dressed again, her shape delicately traced by long, sensitive fingers.

Nobody had ever unnerved her like that before. How could a man like that have a father as sweet and kind as Vincenzo Orsiani?

She was still muttering to herself when she arrived home.

'There's been a phone call from Chris, Rachel,' her mother called as soon as she stepped through the front door. 'He can't make it tonight, something about a meeting.'

'At seven-thirty?' Rachel stopped in surprise and then walked through to the kitchen, glad suddenly to have the evening to herself, to wash her hair, read and clear the Italian out of her mind.

'It's a meeting with a—a . . .' Her mother turned from the fridge, her mind puzzling over a name, and, with a sinking heart, Rachel supplied it.

'A Mr Orsiani?'

'That's it! Of course, Orsiani Italia. My word, Chris will be pleased. Let me know what happened when you see him tomorrow.'

'I will,' Rachel said dully. She could imagine what was going to happen and it wouldn't be anything to rejoice about. Chris was probably going to be replaced by six Italians. And she had told Cynthia not to worry!

Probably the dawning of the wedding day would see both Chris and herself looking for new jobs. No wonder she had felt on the edge of a nightmare; she was probably in it now, a starring role! For Chris to have cancelled their dinner date, he must have received a direct order, for there was so much to discuss about the wedding and tonight they had been going to get down to some hard planning. He was probably in one of the offices right now, feeling as miserable as she did. He would phone later so she would just have to sit and wait; maybe Orsiani would give his cold decision quickly.

Chris didn't phone, though, and his telephone was still ringing at his flat with no answer when Rachel finally gave up and went to bed at eleven, wondering if he had decided to get drunk and then tell her tomorrow that he was out of a job.

CHAPTER TWO

THERE was no sign of the Italian next day and Rachel hurriedly finished the notes, putting them on Bill's desk and escaping thankfully to her own office, eyeing the outer door uneasily. Bill had not come in and he didn't put in an appearance until ten. Even then, he looked deathly and miserable, but he never said anything. Whatever it was, he clearly wasn't going to confide in Rachel and he didn't stay long in the office; in fact, he seemed anxious not to talk to her at all.

After the endless pressure of the previous day, she now found herself with so little to do that she was at a loss to understand it. She rang down to the works but Chris apparently was on a long flight and would not be back until about five, so she had all day to worry about his meeting with Orsiani. She almost wished now that the Italian would come in and hustle her into work, anything to have something to do, but he also was out all day and time dragged heavily.

Chris phoned at five-thirty, just as she was leaving, and he sounded as if he was bursting with high spirits, ready to sing, his happiness soaring.

'Sorry about last night, Rachel,' he said breezily. 'Make it tonight?'

'Yes,' she agreed, breathlessly anxious. 'Chris, what happened?'

'Tell you over dinner. Super news! Can't wait to tell you!' He rang off before she had time to apply any pressure at all and she had to be content to wait until seven-thirty. At any rate, he hadn't been sacked. Maybe he was going to Rome, too? She perked up at that; it was

25

a pleasant thought. A working honeymoon. Six months in Rome and a good excuse to keep her job. She left the office in a better frame of mind than she had on the previous night, shrugging off her worries of yesterday thankfully.

Chris was a few minutes late and came rushing into the foyer of the hotel looking a bit red-eyed but decidedly gleeful.

'Sorry, love! It's been one long rush. God! How that man can go! We were talking until midnight and by the time we'd finished, I felt as if I'd drunk a whole barrel of wine. I could hardly see this morning but he was there on time, eight o'clock sharp, and is he ever sharp!' He took her arm and hurried her into the dining-room, hardly glancing at her in his eagerness and she felt nothing but astonishment.

'You—you are talking about Mr Orsiani?' she asked incredulously, almost running to keep up with him.

'Sure! We had dinner at the Fox. No squalid office for me! Come on, let's eat. I can hardly wait to tell you the great news; I didn't get the chance this morning; Orsiani wanted me to fly him up to Scotland and show him a few of my tricks. It was a great chance to flip in and out of the mountains. I had his hair standing on end a few times, I can tell you.'

Rachel couldn't imagine it. As far as she was concerned, the cold-faced Italian had a monopoly on the ability to make hair stand on end; she only had to think about him to get the beginnings of the feeling herself. She just couldn't see him gripping the seat, his face scared.

'Anyway,' Chris continued, 'it was a good idea. The terrain's pretty similar in many ways so I suppose he knew what he was doing.'

She never doubted it; Orsiani would always know what he was doing. But Chris had her puzzled right now.

'The terrain? Similar to Rome?' She felt as if she had somehow missed a bit of the dialogue. Chris had been talking so fast; it was possible.

'No!' He seated her at the table, almost pushing her into her seat in his burning desire to talk more. 'Zarein! I'm going to Zarein!' There was an unholy joy on his face but Rachel felt any joy she had drain from her in one great lurch of her heart.

She never knew how she got through the next hour. Chris was full of the subject of Zarein, pouring out facts as if he had learned them for a contest. And she didn't need to be told. Zarein had been on the news quite a bit a couple of weeks ago and she had taken a long look at it on television. It looked like an intimate corner of hell, low-lying coastal desert and then nothing else but mountains with desert again behind them. No roads, only rough mule tracks, and temperatures going up to a hundred and thirty at midday, down to five at night. The pictures she had shuddered at on television unfolded in her mind as Chris talked on.

'I'm going to be Operations Manager. Just think about it, Rachel! Responsibility for everything, fly-ing personnel, repairs and service crews, equipment. There'll be six helicopters and they'll have to be kept flying constantly, no slip-ups!'

He was really enjoying it, enjoying his dinner, too, clearly unaware of the despair on Rachel's face. He couldn't seem to stop talking, the words tumbling out one after the other.

'Chris . . .' She tried to make him notice her, to stop him, but it was useless.

'You know they're drilling for oil in the Catel Depression?' he interrupted. 'It was on television about two weeks ago. God! I never realised then that I'd be part of it! It's about a hundred and fifty miles from the coast, hot as hell, a rough circle about fifty miles across and there are going to be four rigs about ten miles apart. The 'copters have to fly in men and take them out again, about two hundred a week, bring in all their food, fuel for the rigs, spare parts. I'll be working about twenty-four hours a day some days, according to Orsiani, but boy, will it be worth it!' He grinned across at her, his face alive with pleasure.

'Where—— What—what about living accommodation?' Rachel asked faintly. It seemed a mundane thing to ask in the face of such glorious acceptance of a posting to hell, but she had to ask something; he'd said nothing that included her.

'Prefabricated huts. No air-conditioning but the men on the rigs are a tough bunch—Americans, Arabs—not nice, but used to roughing it.'

He was speaking with the pride of a captain about his crew of pirates and Rachel realised that he hadn't thought about her once since his meeting with Orsiani. He was planning a future without any consultation with her. She was not even in the picture. He was glorying in the hardships that he personally would have to face as if he were a boy scout on an endurance expedition. A tough bunch, prefabricated huts, no air-conditioning. She felt tears begin to sting her eyes, but Chris never even noticed.

'You realise that if all goes well, if oil is found, we'll be number one in line for the bigger job of servicing the rigs? Orsiani's got great hopes of oil being found; these desert states are floating on the stuff. There'd be more helicopters then, about twenty. I'd get a reputation, be able to pick and choose my next job anywhere in the world!'

Rachel looked down at the dinner she had hardly tasted.

'How—how long is the contract for?' she asked, her

eyes hot with tears.

'Oh, that.' He looked at her at last, ruefully. 'Two years,' he admitted into the silence between them.

'Two years!' She raised unbelieving eyes, eyes that were filled with tears, and his face reddened a little.

''Fraid so, Rachel, love. There's no way you can go out there and I wouldn't let you. We'll have to put the wedding off a bit, I'm afraid.'

He was so nonchalant, so offhand, his mind hardly sparing the time to discuss the end of the wedding, his eyes already far away again, miles into the desert, that she was stunned.

'A bit! Chris, two years is a lifetime!'

'It's not.' He was trying to be soothing, trying to show regret, but he didn't mean it. All she could see was the enthusiasm, as if his consoling tone was a momentary bit of acting that he felt was necessary. He just didn't care! She had been ready to fly at the Italian when he had suggested that she should postpone the wedding for four months, ready to scald him with coffee, boil him in oil; and here was Chris, suggesting that they should wait for two years as if it was a minor matter that could be shrugged off easily, not terribly important, just one of those things.

'It's the chance of a lifetime, Rachel. I've got to think of my future,' he said, suddenly stern.

'Somehow, I thought we were going to share the future,' Rachel accused him shakily. 'I didn't realise that it was just your future.'

He looked embarrassed, struggling with displeasure with her for spoiling his excited talk, for pointing out irritating facts.

'Oh, Rachel! You know what I mean! And the time will fly, honestly it will. You can't go out there—crude sanitation, rough men. Orsiani says it's out of the question for a woman. He says that the firm wouldn't allow it anyway. You've got to realise he's right. I get a month off in every six,' he added by way of a consolation.

'That's four months in two years. We'll be like strangers, Chris,' she whispered.

She could see Orsiani in her mind's eye, the puppet-master pulling the strings. Surely this wasn't because he wanted her to go to Rome with Bill? Surely he wouldn't contemplate doing this so that Bill's party could go to Rome intact, not 'rocking the boat too wildly'? He couldn't! Even as she thought it, she knew that he could. There must be pilots at the Italian end of Orsiani Italia with qualifications as good as Chris's, better, with more experience. If the job was so splendid then somebody at the Italian end would have got it, but that would have left Bill going to Italy without his usual secretary, with a new one. It might have rocked the boat a bit, as he was so used to her, and that would not have suited the cool-eyed Italian.

And anyway, she had angered him, been close to what he would have called insolent. She felt that somebody had her on the end of a chain, the feeling of unreality washing over her as she remembered how she had felt on the edge of a nightmare, part of a dream that she knew nothing about. Cold fingers of fear raced down her spine and she looked at Chris's familiar face as if she had never seen it before, her eyes accusing.

'Hell, Rachel! It's not a death sentence!' He was blusteringly angry, wanting his own way, used to having it, as spoiled as Bill, and she suddenly realised that she came only second in his life, and not even a close second at that; she was way down the list. Chris came first. It was written all over his face.

'Look, in a wartime situation people were separated for longer than two years!' he exclaimed angrily. 'God! I thought you'd be excited,' he added with tightened lips.

'I'm delirious,' Rachel said flatly, misery beginning to numb her. 'In a wartime situation, neither party has any choice. I got the chance for six months in Rome yesterday, Chris. I turned it down. I—I was even angry that it had been offered.'

'This is different, Rachel!' he looked at her in exasperation. 'You're only a secretary and you'll be giving up work anyway. This is my future!' His voice rose, and so did Rachel.

'You've told me that twice, Chris,' she said quietly, picking up her bag. 'I'd like to go home please.'

He didn't please, there was no mistaking that. He flung down his napkin with a childish gesture and clearly he had to restrain himself from walking off and leaving her. He had wanted her to be as enthusiastic as he was and, even now, she felt guilty that she hadn't been, even now it seemed to be somehow her fault, a thing to stay heavily on her conscience.

She had spoiled him just as she and Margaret spoiled Bill, and he had dismissed her misery in a flare of self-righteous anger. He wasn't pleased either when she went stiff and icy in his arms as he tried to kiss her goodnight, and she stood on the doorstep as his car drove off. Even the engine sounded angry, petulant, aggrieved. She had laid down no ultimatums, asked nothing, and he certainly had offered nothing.

She was suddenly and sickenly aware that he did not love her, had never really loved her. His mind was on the future, his future, the glamour of promotion and a big name for himself. He was as angry as a schoolboy whose daring escapade has been questioned by a cautious adult. And looming in the background, in the back of her mind, chilly and icy, watching with indifferent interest, was the cold-faced, grey-eyed Italian, Orsiani.

Rachel didn't go in to work the next day. She had spent

most of the night crying and she couldn't face the office, couldn't face anyone. Her mother had been a little stunned at the news but soon turned it round to the same old theme.

'Well, at least he didn't wait until you were married and pregnant before leaving. Your father did. He's better than your father in that respect.'

'I thought he loved me, I really did,' Rachel whispered, half to herself, red-eyed and worn out, feeling that there was nowhere to turn.

'Men don't know the meaning of the word,' her mother asserted. 'It's been all on your side, obviously. I can't say that I'm surprised. You can forget love where a man's concerned; it's always the same.'

Rachel didn't even ring in to work. She spent the day thinking, trying to decide what was the best thing to do, trying to rid herself of the feeling that Chris had deliberately given her that in some unlikely way it was all her fault, that she had let him down. She had no doubts about his feelings for her, though, and it hurt badly. He had not even wanted to discuss the future except to say vaguely that everything would have to be postponed.

When he came round after work she had made her decision. It was hers to make, and her feelings during the day had grown into a deep certainty that the love was all on her side. She had been a good companion, an efficient helper and now she was an obstacle in the way as Chris went on to greater glory. If he had loved her he would have not been able to face two years of separation any more than she could, but it was not only that; his attitude had told her only too well just what she was in his life. Her faith in anything was badly shaken, so was her pride, and she knew that it would be a long time before she could trust anyone again.

'I think we should call the whole thing off, Chris. We should cancel the wedding. You—you don't know what your future holds. There—there may be someone else who comes along.' She looked away quickly at the look in his eyes. The idea wasn't entirely a shock to him, she could tell that. The world was now his oyster and there were other women, other countries, without being tied down. It was written so clearly on his face that she knew her decision had been right.

'I'm not going to look for anyone else, Rachel, sweetheart, but you're being sensible as usual. In two years we'll begin again.'

She couldn't turn back to face him. For three years they had been planning and saving for the wedding, everything thought out, the furniture chosen, a deposit put down on the house. This week they had been going to get down to the final plans, and now . . .

'By the way, Rachel, I've been thinking,' he said into the silence that hung between them. 'Maybe we should close the joint account and split up the money. I could do with the extra cash as a safety float and you could spend your half on a bit of glamour. We shan't need it in two years' time. I'll be rolling in money,' he added with a laugh.

'Good idea. I'll see to it in the morning, unless you want to?'

'Heavens, no! You've always dealt with things like that. I'll pick it up in the office after lunch. I've signed a note for the bank in case you need it.'

So much for spur-of-the-moment thoughts, Rachel noticed bitterly, and yes, she had always been the one to do things, the one to take the responsibility.

He suggested that they should go out for a drink and Rachel was pleased to go. She felt that she had nothing to say to Chris now and when he suggested, too, that as time was so short they should perhaps not see each other again before he went, so that the parting would be easier, she agreed lifelessly.

Truth to tell, she was thinking about another man, a tearing anger inside her. She was thinking about a cool-eyed stranger who had torn her life apart and left her not knowing what to do.

She hardly heard the light-hearted chatter that Chris kept going to ease his own embarrassment; her mind was completely on a tall, dark man with silver-grey eyes that were as icy and frozen as the Arctic wastes. She would hate him to the end of her days. She had been blissfully unaware of the slender balance that held her happiness together, totally unprepared for the shattering of her plans and her future, and the Italian had walked in and interfered, forcing everything out into the open, making her see things she would never have seen, things she didn't want to see. She blamed him as she could never blame Chris. Chris was weak and selfish and he loved himself more than anyone, but he was not the devil. Orsiani was that!

Bill Taylor looked up as she came into his office the next day, coming round the desk to stand in front of her, suddenly not plaintive any more.

'Are you all right, Rachel?'

'Yes. I'm sorry about yesterday, sorry I didn't let you know.' She felt a burst of guilt that she had left him to face Orsiani alone, but, on looking a second time at his grim face, she thought that, after all, he'd probably managed. He didn't look as if he had suffered any real hardship; he just looked annoyed and upset.

'It's all right. I didn't really expect to see you.' There was an angry gleam in his eyes as he looked at her pale face. Even the most uninterested observer could have told that she had not spent a happy day yesterday, that today she was still filled with shock and misery.

'I was at that damned meeting with Chris and Orsiani,' he suddenly burst out. 'It was like watching somebody bargaining for a soul. I knew about it before you, Rachel. That's why I kept out of the office the other day, because I couldn't tell you; it was up to Chris to do that. Anyway, I was hoping he'd come to his senses and turn it down. He didn't though, did he?' he demanded angrily.

For a moment, she almost told him to mind his own business, but he was only upset on her behalf and nothing could fool him at this moment. Why not admit it? Everyone would know soon enough.

'No. The wedding's off, permanently.'

Bill sucked in an angry breath, swearing softly to himself. 'The heartless dog!'

She wasn't sure if he meant Chris or Orsiani, and she didn't care at that moment. She was protected by the numbness of shock and the weariness of long bouts of weeping. She didn't need the arms that Bill put around her, the fatherly hug he gave her, but it was a kindly thought and he patted the bright head that he had pulled against his shoulder.

Of course, the Italian chose that moment to walk into the office, his face icy at the scene that he obviously thought he was witnessing, but Bill was too annoyed to care and Rachel was too numb. Bill's arm remained round her shoulders, his hand making curious little patting motions as if he was comforting a small child.

'Make us some coffee, Rachel, love,' he growled, 'and see that you take it easy today.' He shot a glaring glance at Orsiani that told him to leave her well alone and it gave Rachel a fleeting feeling of warmth that somebody understood and cared.

Certainly her mother didn't understand. The whole affair seemed to have brought back the bitter past, and Rachel had been glad to come to work. She didn't want to hear any more that a man found a woman ungainly and ugly when she was pregnant. She didn't want to hear about her father's sins, about men in general. She wanted silence, peace, numbess, nothing.

She had the tray in her hands when Bill came out of the office, closing the door with a deliberately heavy hand.

'You'd better drink my coffee, Rachel,' he grated, lifting the cup off the tray and putting it on her desk. 'He'll have his, but I'm needed in the works, apparently. He's found a flaw.'

She had never really seen him angry before, he usually only grumbled pitifully, and she realised that his anger was over her. Bill was hurting for her and it somehow lessened her hurt, made it more bearable. She managed a smile and went into the other room as Bill left, her face still, her eyes far away, almost in a daze, forgetting for a moment who was in there. This morning everything had receded to a painful dream quality; even her anger had become numbed.

'Your coffee, Mr Orsiani.' Her voice was dull, almost flat, every action purely automatic, her creamy face lifeless, her glorious hair seeming to be dulled to match her spirit as she put the cup on the desk and turned to leave, wondering vaguely if she would ever have feelings again.

His voice stopped her, making her look up slowly.

'Rachel.' It was a curiously husky sound and she wondered blankly what he wanted, why he was using her first name when he disliked her so much.

'Yes, sir?'

'*Dio!* Will you stop calling me that?' There was a faint flush across his cheekbones and she stared at him in surprise.

'I'm sorry, Mr Orsiani,' she said dully, looking away, waiting to hear what he wanted but ready to leave.

'And don't . . .' He looked furiously frustrated as if there was a language barrier, although he had no difficulty with English, whatever he wanted to say. 'I was merely about to remark that you were not here yesterday. You were ill?'

'No.' She shook her head faintly, the soft bright hair brushing her cheeks. 'I just didn't want to come in to work.'

The flat statement seemed to leave him speechless. For once something had stopped him in his tracks, taken his breath away.

'Do you normally just stay away, as the mood takes you?'

'No.' She looked up at him again then, beginning to come back to life a little, beginning to remember who had instigated all this misery. Right now, she didn't feel as if she had escaped from something that would have been a disaster. Maybe she would later when the hurt had gone but, right now, Chris and his crimes seemed to fade into the distance and she felt anger rising inside her, bringing her back to life as she faced the enemy before her, a man who had cold-bloodedly changed the course of a life he would never have anything further to do with, because she wasn't going to Rome. 'No,' she repeated, her voice stronger. 'But then, I don't normally cancel a marriage completely. It's not the sort of thing one can get much practice in, is it?'

For a second he just stared at her silently and then he said, 'You are not now going to marry Pearson?'

'Isn't it what you expected, Mr Orsiani? You painted a pretty grim picture of Zarein, I understand. A happy honeymoon with scruffy men, scorching heat, no sanitation and the desert moon! Still, as Orsiani Italia wouldn't permit a wife there anyway, there's not really a lot of point in being a wife at the moment.'

He didn't like the tone of her voice, but then she hadn't expected him to.

'It is not a life sentence! He is going on a two-year contract and we will release him at the end of it,' he said scathingly. 'Perhaps I should point out, as in some strange way I seem to be taking the blame for his desertion, that he was not obliged to go.'

'What did he have as a choice, dismissal?' Rachel asked, her voice rising, not caring who he was any more.

'No, he did not! We needed someone out there; I offered him the job. He accepted. He accepted, Miss Gordon, immediately. Apparently he did not need to consult you; he said you would be delighted.' His eyebrows rose sarcastically over the cool grey eyes.

'Oh, I am!' she snapped. 'So delighted that I've called off my wedding. I could jump about laughing!'

He was watching her closely, seeing the tears of bitterness and anger begin to form in her brown eyes, but she rushed on, too hurt to care if he sacked her on the spot, hating him with a pent-up fury that wanted to claw at him.

'You did it on purpose, didn't you? You couldn't face it that your neat little plans were not going to work! You move people like chessmen!'

'My plans for the move to Rome were made weeks ago,' he said sharply. 'I had no idea that you were engaged to the helicopter pilot until I arrived, but I certainly do not make it a practice to alter my plans to fit in with a daydream of a wedding!'

'That's what you think of a wedding? A daydream!' she shouted.

'Yours was,' he said coldly. 'A romantic girl wishing to marry a man who cares more about a machine and a career.'

'You—you bastard!' she whispered, her face white. He took a threatening step towards her but it seemed that the tears now rolling silently down her face held back any violence that was in him. He was wildly angry though; she could see that even through her tears.

'I had no idea before I came that you were engaged,' he repeated harshly. 'And you wear no ring. I saw no reason when I first came here why the team should not stay intact.'

'We decided against a ring,' Rachel muttered, her unhappiness flooding further forward. 'We decided to save the money and spend it on the house.'

'How very romantic. I understand your distress,' he said cuttingly. 'He's a real hero. What will you do now?' he continued before she could fly at him again.

'Well, I shan't come to Rome, you can bank on that. The team can go without me, so your efforts have been a waste of time.'

'I rarely waste my time, *signorina*,' he rasped, 'and whether you go to Rome or not is immaterial to me. In spite of your insolence I would have been willing to take you with us when we leave, but if you wish to stay here in this grey little place and remain unhappy, then the decision is all yours to make.'

For some unfathomable reason, the thought of them all going off without her filled her with pain. Anger had sustained her for a while, but now the finality in his voice left her feeling strangely lonely and it was all too much. She dropped her head into her hands and sobbed, her pent-up emotions welling over.

'Rachel! Try not to be so unhappy. It will pass. Come with me to Rome; forget this idiot who doesn't care about you.'

She found herself pulled into iron-strong arms as her body shook with misery, arms that were oddly comforting, frighteningly comforting, and she pulled frantically away, terrified by the sudden urge she had felt to lean against him and let him hold her.

'Your—your coffee, is on the desk, Mr Orsiani,' she managed, choking back the sobs. 'It's going cold.'

'Let it,' he said quietly, watching her with intent grey eyes. 'And my name is Nick.'

'So is the devil's,' she flared, wanting to strike out at somebody, hating him for the things he had said that she knew deep down were true, blaming him for things that he had no control over.

'You bad-tempered little vixen!' She saw her mistake as fury surged into the silvery eyes and he hauled her against him, his fingers like steel, biting into her shoulders. 'You are blaming me because your doting fiancé prefers to further his career than to stay with you.'

'We'll get married when he comes back!' she cried wildly, looking up into the blaze of his angry eyes, lying to ease her own hurt pride.

'Maybe by then he'll have gone too far up in the world,' he said nastily, his stormy grey eyes narrowed. 'Perhaps a very lowly secretary will seem less of an exciting prospect when the oil strike comes and the television crews from Italy are interviewing the daring helicopter pilots and their local boss. Perhaps, then, London, Paris and Rome and the glamour of the ladies there will appeal to him more!'

She pulled free, stepped back and hit him hard, a slap that should have rocked his head but which didn't even make him flinch. But she saw now a fury that could far outclass any fury of her own. She spun round to escape but the steel-like fingers jerked her round to face him.

'You fiery little bitch!' he whispered with terrifying quiet, his teeth clenched in rage. 'Your selfish fiancé is no match for you, is he? He needs a mother, someone to assure him that he is always doing well, someone to encourage his antics. Perhaps you have struck him and got away with it, perhaps that is how you have chastised him, but I am not a light-hearted, empty-headed boy to be corrected. If there is correcting needed between us, I will do the correcting!'

His mouth came down on hers with a savagery that frightened her into stillness. His unyielding hands were digging into her, crushing the bones of her shoulders even through the material of her jacket and she knew that if he didn't stop soon, she would faint.

He did stop. He lifted his head and looked down into her shocked face with menacing quiet, his eyes dark and still.

'Mr Orsiani, please!' she managed a whispered plea and he let her go, turning away abruptly to the desk, his hands thrust into his pockets, his tall frame taut and still.

For a second, she stood shaking, and then she fled, slamming the door, racing off to the ladies' room, hoping that no one would see her and notice the state she was in.

She stared at herself in the mirror in disbelief. Her hair was a mess, her face streaked with tears, but her eyes were too bright to believe and her breasts were full and tight, straining against her blouse. She didn't dare to even think about it. She had never been in a situation in her ordinary life before when every alarm bell inside had started to ring. When she had first seen the tall Italian, her body's reactions had been purely instinctive, primitive. She told herself fiercely that this was what was wrong, half-convincing herself. It wasn't every day that she was attacked by a savage!

Chris came in immediately after lunch. She had spent the morning getting on with her work, Orsiani nowhere to be seen, her nerves steadying when she realised that he had left the office while she was in the ladies' room. He might be ashamed of himself, but she doubted it. When she came back from lunch there was still silence from Bill's room and she assumed that Bill was still busy sorting out the 'flaw', no doubt with Orsiani breathing down his neck.

She had the money ready for Chris and it was so

obvious that he wanted to get everything cleared, his past wiped out, her with it, that she felt an urgent need to help him and see the last of him before the misery came flooding back. Oddly enough, her encounter with the Italian earlier had shocked her out of her numb and unhappy state into a sort of startled life and, now, to look at Chris and believe all that had happened between them was almost impossible.

He looked just the same, the same man who had come so swiftly and quietly into her office so many times to snatch her up and kiss her unexpectedly. Now, he just wanted to be off, to rub the slate clean, and she was thankful that she had the money ready. As she gave it to him, he hesitated for a second, but only for a second.

'It's not the end, Rachel, you know. We'll start again. I'll be rolling in money and we'll never have any worries. I might even start up on my own.'

'I know.' She managed a brilliant smile. All dreams, daydreams, a boy's delight. 'Well—see you in two years, then.'

'Right!' He grinned across at her, his conscience eased. ''Bye, Rachel, love.' He leaned across to kiss her but she managed to turn her face, taking the quick kiss on her cheek, and then he was gone, cheerfully, happily, with no remorse.

'You were returning the "ring", I see.'

She looked up to see just what she had expected to see, the tall Italian lounging in Bill's doorway, his arms folded across his chest. She wondered just how long he had been there. She had not had any idea that he was even in the building; he moved about so silently that he could appear from nowhere, it seemed.

'If you wish to think of it like that, yes,' she snapped, turning away, her face flushed. There was no reason to be polite to him, she told herself; he had stepped outside

the bounds of that kind of relationship. She didn't want
to look at him again. He was another man without
remorse. Her lips were still tingling, but apparently he
had written off the incident. It made her temper flare.

'I'm sorry that I was talking in the firm's time, Mr
Orsiani,' she added spitefully. 'I'll stay late and make it
up if you could tell me how long I was talking to Chris.'

He was behind her and she had never even heard him
move.

'Ten minutes,' he said, soft and low. 'Ten minutes too
long.' He spun her round and she looked up with a gasp.

'Mr Orsiani—please!' She was expecting another
attack, but the clear, grey eyes were not angry.

'Nick,' he corrected softly, his hands moulding her
shoulders. 'Nick, even if it is also the devil's name.'

She found herself staring into his eyes as she had done
when she had first seen him, the frightening feelings
racing through her again, and she didn't need to look
down to know that her breasts had surged forward,
sharp and hard against her blouse.

He looked down and then raised his head slowly, his
eyes beginning to darken.

'That is the third time that you have paid me that
particular compliment, *signorina*,' he said softly. 'I
excite you.'

'You—you do not!' she gasped, struggling to get free,
wondering how he dared behave like this.

'I do,' he asserted quietly. 'You have a quick and
clever tongue, but you cannot talk yourself out of this.
Your body is signalling me too strongly.'

She could hardly believe that this was happening to
her. Maybe in Italy men who were almost strangers
talked like this to women, but here it was an insult. He
didn't seem to know that and, as she strained to get
away, her face flushed with embarrassment and anger,
he threaded his fingers through her hair, his eyes on the

shining bright strands, his touch unbelievably gentle.

'Such astonishingly beautiful hair,' he murmured softly. His glance moved to her flushed and angry face. 'Such a beautiful, fiery creature. You need someone to tame you, *signorina*, someone to school you like a fiery, thoroughbred filly. You need gentling into obedience.'

She just stared at him, her eyes enormous in her face, and he smiled slowly at her sudden quiet, his eyes running along her mouth as if he were stroking her lips.

'I would rather not hurt you,' he said softly as his mouth moved swiftly and claimed hers before she could pull out of her dazed disbelief.

Feelings shot through her like an electrical charge, starting at her toes and racing through her body as his mouth moved over hers with a soft, sweet urgency that deepened and deepened until she hardly knew where she was.

One hand still in her hair, his other moved to the small of her back, pulling her relentlessly towards him, and she gave a little choked sound as her body came into contact with the hard, powerful masculine frame, her mind shocked at the surge of desire she felt in him and at the quick sound of satisfaction he made deep in his throat as he felt her close to him.

She found without warning that she was cradled against his shoulder, his hands moving over her back with an ease and familiarity that shocked her further. He was making no effort to disguise his feelings, the unending kiss an excuse to hold her close and allow his hands to move over her as his eyes had moved over her when he had first arrived. And when he raised his head and looked down into her dazed and shocked eyes, she was too stunned to even try to move away.

She wondered hysterically what Bill would say if he suddenly came in and found her wrapped in the arms of a stranger, a man who had so obviously been allowed to follow his animal instincts and fondle her as if she was a possession, but she couldn't seem to move; she just went on staring blindly into the glittering eyes that had darkened with pleasure.

'I will tame you, Rachel,' he said with a soft triumph. 'I will hold you in my arms and soothe away your temper, turn your fire to more pleasant things.'

A cold shiver seemed to run right down her spine at the quiet triumph she heard, because now she understood the way he had looked at her when he had first seen her, now she understood why Chris was promoted and despatched to Zarein. She realised now the concealed desire in those cold silvery eyes that had stripped her naked. He wanted her! He had moved with ruthless determination to remove the obstacle in his path: her wedding!

The fact that Chris had been more than willing to go was now irrelevant. The fact that she had found out that he did not love her, that at any time in the future when something should be attractive enough to lure him away he would have gone, did not enter her mind at all at that moment. All she could see was that this man had interfered with her life, determinedly, ruthlessly and with a speed that even now left her feeling that it must be unreal. No wonder she had felt on the edge of a nightmare, no wonder she had seemed to be in a dream that belonged to someone else. The triumph in his voice, the desire in his hands, told her all she wanted to know. This was not a man who allowed such foolish things as convention and decent behaviour to stand in his path. He was powerful, dynamic, head of a giant firm. He would not be accustomed to being thwarted.

She felt a rising triumph of her own. She had a stick with which to beat the devil and she would use it unmercifully. He would remember the name Rachel Gordon, long after he had forgotten any other woman.

'You will come with me to Rome, Rachel?' he asked softly, steadying her as she swayed, straightening her hair, her blouse, with possessive fingers.

'Yes.' She said it with a demure little sigh, her eyes downcast, and he immediately tilted her face, his eyes still darkened with desire but watchful, keenly intelligent.

Then he laughed, a low murmur of amusement and, rather frighteningly, a sound of delight.

'You will play a dangerous game with me, *signorina*?' he enquired softly. 'You will play it on my territory with my rules? Do not forget that only one can win and that the winner takes all.' He looked down at the evidence of her body with a slow enjoyment that brought wild colour into her face. 'You, too, feel a desire and so the odds are even.' He met her eyes, eyes that were now a little worried and seemed to be filling her face. 'I am willing to play your game. The prize could become an obsession!'

CHAPTER THREE

THEY were working in the main offices of Orsiani Italia, an imposing building in the centre of Rome, and Rachel found that, after three weeks there, it was very difficult to sustain the anger and bitterness that had prompted her to accept the move to Italy.

There was a light-hearted air to the whole city that penetrated even into the quiet, sumptuous offices. A kind of bubbling excitement that lingered in the air. There was blossom on the trees, the sun was shining, everybody seemed to be happy and even Bill became noticeably more cheerful, his grumbles rare once he had discovered an unexpected ability to cope.

Margaret and the children loved it. They had a huge ground-floor flat in a luxurious house on the outskirts of the city and the children were in a small International School nearby.

Nobody, it seemed, had anything to worry about, and the small, tight-faced English party that had arrived tired and weary at the airport three weeks ago was now a part of Orsiani Italia, almost totally integrated and clearly not relishing the idea of a return to England ever.

It seemed that only Rachel was uneasy. Nothing had gone as she had imagined it in her angry and hurt acceptance of the move to Rome. She had been sure that Nick Orsiani would pursue her, would give her the satisfaction of leading him on and then dropping him flat, but he had ignored her.

He was in the same building and she saw him almost every day. The offices were open-plan, richly carpeted, fitted with every conceivable modern device. At first she

47

had been shocked to think that there would be no privacy, no place to call her own, and Bill Taylor had been furious, but they both soon realised that they were in fact completely private. There was space; each alcove contained a separate office bigger than any that either of them had ever worked in before. The whole floor was given over to this arrangement and the luxury was very tempting.

Nick Orsiani was the only one with a completely closed-in office and he was in it every day, working as hard as anyone else. She often saw him striding past, intent on the notes in his hand or talking with one of the managers but, although he sometimes caught her eye and nodded a greeting, it was no more than a greeting he gave to any of the other secretaries.

Finally, her initial feeling of suspicion and frustration that she couldn't get sufficiently close to him to make the kill changed to bewilderment. She found herself surreptitiously watching for a glimpse of him, her eyes secretly on the tall, powerful frame, the glossy black hair, the lean brown hands that moved constantly as he talked, emphasising a point he was making.

She began to notice other things, too: the way he shrugged lazily and laughed; the way he tilted his head sideways, faintly smiling as he listened to something that any of the secretaries had to say; the way his eyes narrowed and crinkled in amusement and the way they could bring a blush to the cheeks of any of the typists on the floor or even the most staid and elderly of the secretaries.

His eyes never narrowed in amusement at her, though. She merely got the polite nod, until she had to work hard to keep the surprise from her face. She had spent most of her half of the money that she and Chris had saved in doing exactly what he had suggested; buying herself some glamour. She now had more clothes than she had ever had in her life, beautiful clothes that enhanced the red-gold of her hair and made her slender figure alluring. She had been careful to choose them, thinking angrily that they would be part of the lure to trap Nick Orsiani, but he never even noticed.

She was noticed in the streets, though. Sometimes it seemed that every man in Rome had taken a personal interest in her. Wherever she walked there were admiring glances, low whistles, cars slowing down to blare their horns at her, until she seriously contemplated not going out at all.

She mentioned her predicament to one of the Italian managers, getting a burst of laughter and eyebrows raised in surprise.

'It is merely admiration, *signorina*. You are in Rome and it is our habit, especially with that unusual hair. Give them a cheerful smile and go on your way. Nothing will happen except that you will make their day.' He had managed to look seductive even with a bald head and spectacles and an age that wouldn't see fifty again, so she gave it a try. It worked, and her walks in the city lost their nightmare quality. She no longer felt harassed.

On Saturday, Rachel was strolling along shopping, when, one after the other, three cars slowed beside her, the low whistles she now expected floating across the sunny pavement. The smile worked as usual and the worst thing that happened was one rather leering wink.

The fourth car, however, stopped, and Nick Orsiani got out, striding round the front of it and opening the passenger door.

'Get in!' He looked furious and she came to a halt in front of him as he towered over her, his striped sports shirt tight across a powerful chest that was rising and falling with bottled in rage, his strong legs in white jeans planted squarely in front of her barring any further progress on her part.

She just looked at him in astonishment and he jerked his thumb to the car.

'Get in!'

'Thank you, but I'm enjoying the sunshine.'

'Enjoy it in the car!' She was hustled in before she could protest and found herself being driven through the traffic at a furious speed before she could draw breath.

'I have no desire to ride in your car, Mr Orsiani!' she snapped, tensing in panic as a car cut across their path and he never slackened speed, merely blasting his horn in true Roman style.

'It's Saturday, my free time. I was strolling along enjoying myself. I am not enjoying myself now!'

'I saw you strolling along,' he rasped, his furious grey eyes on the road. 'If you need to supplement your income, *signorina*, there is no need to encourage every rogue in Italy! Just tell me how much you need and I will give it to you at once!'

His meaning dawned on her very rapidly and only the thought of a dreadful accident in the racing traffic stopped her from flying at him then and there.

'How—how dare you! Pull over! I want to get out.'

'I'm quite sure that you do,' he grated, swinging the car round a corner almost on two wheels. She was astonished when she realised that they were in the road where she lived, almost at the house where she had her flat, and alarmed when she also realised that, though he had never asked, he knew exactly where she lived.

'You are home!' he ground out through clenched white teeth. 'I do not wish to see you ever again idly walking the streets, smiling beguilingly at any perspiring motorist looking for a cheap thrill or a companion for the night!'

'For your information,' she raged, red-faced at his obvious beliefs, 'I was advised to do just that by one of

your own managers when I complained about the
behaviour of Italian men! Not that I was particularly
surprised at the behaviour of Italian men!'

'Tell me the name of this idiot!' he snapped, turning
towards her, his eyes flashing silver sparks. 'He will not
be one of my managers by Monday afternoon!'

'I'll tell you no such thing!' she stated firmly,
beginning to get more than a little worried by the
violence of a temper that appeared to be only just under
control. 'Just leave me alone and let me go on imagining
that you're in another part of the world!'

'You have been imagining that, *signorina*?' Without
warning his anger had disappeared; he was as smooth
and silky as a huge cat. 'I have not paid enough attention
to you? You walk the streets of Rome because you are
lonely? I had imagined that the game we agreed to play
would have fully occupied such an agile mind.'

Rachel stifled the quick flicker of fear, the uneasy
feeling that she was outclassed, had been outman-
oeuvred. He was waiting, curiously tense as if ready to
pounce, and she felt a quick breathlessness.

'There is no game, Mr Orsiani,' she asserted with a
calmness that she certainly didn't feel. 'The things
that—that happened in a moment of anger are now a
good many weeks away from us, and—and it was just
foolish.'

'You cannot withdraw from a game once it has
started, *signorina*,' he remarked, giving her a mocking
look. 'Unless, of course, you wish to concede the game.
But I did point out to you that the winner takes all.'

'There is no game, Mr Orsiani!' she snapped,
beginning to feel even more breathless, and alarmed to
find that he had moved closer, his arm across her,
resting on the door, trapping her into the close confines
of the car. 'We—we said things that we didn't mean.
We've spent three weeks behaving perfectly normally

and I wish that you'd let the matter drop.'

'You wish me to concede defeat, *signorina*?' He laughed, his eyebrows raised in surprise. 'I never accept defeat. As to the game, it is well under way. You may have been dreaming a little but I have been playing the game since we arrived at the scene of the contest. You seem to have lost a few points. Perhaps you are not trying and wish to lose? Perhaps that is why you are roaming about the streets so wistfully? Merely announce your surrender and I will take you back to my flat; neither of us has ever been in any doubt as to what the prize is.'

'Let me out!' Rachel pushed his arm away and jerked the door open, almost falling out, then ran along the path and up to the house, turning for one frightened and outraged look as he started the car, the engine purring softly.

'*Arrivederci, signorina*,' he called softly. 'You will need another plan, I think. A better one.'

She went in and slammed the door, dashing up to her second-floor flat and sitting down with a scared feeling that her legs would collapse if she tried to stand again.

What did he mean, he had been playing the game? He'd done nothing, ignored her. And got her restless and worried, she realised, her eyes widening, got her so that she couldn't take her eyes off him, so that she had begun to notice everything about him. Yes, he had gained a few points. Well, well, well . . .

On Monday morning she re-arranged her desk, giving a feeble excuse to Bill that he hardly noticed. She moved her chair then, putting her back to the open network of offices, shutting off the sight of anyone who passed by. She couldn't see him now, not even by accident. He could admire the back of her head. She managed to remain without even a glimpse of him until Wednesday, feeling gleeful and very much more sure of herself.

On Wednesday morning, Bill had left the office just
before lunch on some errand in the city and Rachel was
left to struggle alone. Naturally their work was in
English, but it was still a little difficult as they were
dealing with the marketing of the Orsiani products to
English-speaking countries and the work was new to
her.

She had to concentrate hard and even then she was on
edge, afraid to make a mistake and make a fool of herself
in front of everyone. This was not the rather quiet little
place she had been used to, a place she had grown into,
and for all she knew Nick Orsiani would use any mistake
to berate her in front of everyone.

She suddenly realised that she couldn't read one vital
sentence, and small wonder as it was in Italian.

'Oh!' She looked wildly around but there was no one
to turn to, almost everyone had left for lunch. And she
wasn't going to go trotting around looking into alcoves
saying, 'Please!'

She dived across to Bill's desk. He had already started
to learn the language with an enthusiasm that startled
her. He and Margaret went to classes twice a week and
his new dictionary went with him from home to office
and back again.

Even with it on her desk, even with a notepad and
pencil, it was hopeless. She felt really frustrated and
almost ready to scream. No doubt this was another
Orsiani trick to unsettle her and make her feel less than
human. No doubt he had ordered this little meanness,
she thought angrily, knowing full well that the papers in
question had never even been near him yet and probably
never would, but if there was someone to blame then he
was the most blamable person in the world.

Without warning, two arms came down beside her,
brown hands flat on her desk, one at each side, blue shirt
sleeves brushing against her bare arms as she gave a

quick and cautious glance sideways.

'You are having trouble, *signorina*?' Nick Orsiani's voice purred almost in her ear as he leaned over her. 'I will translate.'

He wrote out the words in English on her notepad but seemed in no hurry to straighten up. 'I understand that you are the only one who is not attempting to learn the language,' he observed softly. 'You have sufficiently good reason? Remember that I want anyone of importance to speak both languages.'

'Well, I'm not important,' she said as tartly as she could manage, being too scared to move as his body was so close to hers. A move in any direction would bring them into closer contact, unless she sprang up and heaved him away. She didn't fancy that. She knew that violence with Nick Orsiani could bring rapid punishment; in fact, she suspected that it was a certainty. 'I'm merely a lowly secretary, as you once informed me,' she continued, deciding to rely on her tongue. 'Anyway, I'll never need it again. I'll go to another firm when my six months here is over, and Italian's too difficult for someone as lowly and stupid as I am, so I don't go to lessons.'

She felt quite pleased with that until the blue-sleeved arms moved a little closer, trapping her firmly.

'It is not difficult,' he murmured softly into her hair. 'I will teach you, a little every night, as you lie in my bed.'

She gasped with shock and would have jumped up then but he beat her to it, taking her arm and swinging her easily to her feet.

'Get your bag. You're having lunch with me,' he pronounced firmly.

'I don't want . . .' She looked up into eyes that were brimming with laughter and got no further because he said,

'You do want but you are too stubborn to admit it, too intent on your angry little game. Well, as you have scored points this week by skilfully manoeuvring your furniture, we will call it a draw so far. Now we move the game on to a higher plane. In any case, I now know the shape of the back of your head off by heart. You will be forced to face me across the luncheon table. Your back is beautiful but I prefer the front view, I must confess.'

He called airily to Bill, who had just then walked in, that he was taking Rachel out to lunch and Bill beamed. She could have hit them both. To avoid an angry scene, she had to go meekly along, irritated by the light but very firm grip on her arm, conscious again of the odd burning sensation that the long fingers brought to her skin.

They were getting quite a few interested looks from the people who were still in the building and Rachel wished that he would let go of her arm. If he had been content to simply walk beside her it would have been less obvious that they were together, but clearly he thought that if he slackened his grip she would pull free and race away out of sight.

No doubt everyone was thinking that she was a willing prey. He didn't seem to be the sort of man who took any secretary out to lunch, not even his own secretary, and from some of the looks she was getting it was embarrassingly obvious that they thought she was a little interest to pass his time with; no doubt they imagined that she was already his night-time companion!

Her embarrassment was complete when he stopped for a lengthy discussion with one of his managers and still held possessively to her arm. She didn't even understand what they were saying, and she didn't know where to look to avoid all the interest.

Once outside the building, Nick turned sharply into a sunlit square, traffic free and oddly peaceful.

'You have been here before?' he enquired as she looked around at the small, expensive little shops, the tempting restaurants, the old woman with a basket of flowers sitting under a tree by the fountain.

'No. It's lovely, like another world.'

He nodded, releasing her arm and walking silently beside her.

'It's all right,' he agreed. 'So long as you remember that not all places in Rome are all right; so long as you know where you are going. You would be surprised and no doubt very shocked to find some very poor quarters not too far from here. It is not a good idea to wander around alone.'

'I'm quite used to taking care of myself,' she said a trifle sharply, thinking that he was harking back to the motorists and her walk through the streets. 'I'm a big girl now.'

He took her remark at face value; probably the idiom was too much even for his perfect English. His eyes skimmed over her slender figure and he didn't look either amused or reassured.

'You are tall,' he conceded, 'but you are very slender. The bones in your shoulders seem almost fragile. Do not overestimate your ability to look after yourself. Some of these people who live not too far away are very nice, kindly; some are predators, reared on the streets with the ability to survive and the savagery of a wild animal.'

She blushed at his mention of her fragile bones. She had almost forgotten the kiss of a few weeks ago and his remarks brought it all back, including the queer, tight little burst of pain inside her. 'I'm not really stupid, you know,' she said more sharply than she intended. 'I've no idea why you're telling me all this.'

'Because I saw your great big beautiful eyes looking with eager inquisitiveness down the narrow streets that lead off the square, *signorina*,' he said, just as sharply. 'I imagine that you are planning to come here at some time alone. Here in the square and in the main streets you are safe. Venture too far afield and you are not safe at all.' He glanced at her keenly. 'You are impetuous, the sort of girl who acts on impulse. You acted on impulse in coming to Rome at all when you had no fancy for it, and at this moment my impulse is to send you back to England, for your own safety.'

This would not have suited her at all; she had not made one move to extract her revenge. Thinking about it, all the success seemed to have been on his part. He even took light-heartedly the idea that she was seeking a revenge, dismissing it as if it was some whim of hers to be coy and cautious about being captured. It was beginning to get to her a little, too, his attitude. There were times when she found herself thinking that he was really not as bad as she had at first thought, and then she had to remind herself forcefully that he had stepped into her life and altered the course of it merely because he had felt a burst of desire. She doubted if he felt it now or he would have been pursuing her more savagely. He was merely indulging in a pleasant pastime of pretending to be locked in combat with her, taking up the thread of the game, as he called it, when he was at a loose end.

'I promise not to go wandering vaguely about,' she said hastily, looking up at him with wide innocent eyes, receiving suddenly a cold grey stare before he nodded, partly satisfied.

'Very well. I'll try to believe you, *signorina*. It would not suit me to send you back to England yet. I have other plans for you.'

That silenced her, and when she glanced at him warily he was grinning to himself, his eyes roaming idly around the square.

They had lunch in a little restaurant tucked well away into a quiet corner of the sunlit square, eating at a table just inside the door where she could watch the passers-by, although most of her time was occupied by Nick Orsiani, trying to guard against the skilful net of his charm and courtesy, trying to look for a chink in his armour instead of sitting there simply looking at him.

Even the way he ate was a delight to watch, she thought with irritation as he demolished his spaghetti with the ease of a lifetime's practice, grinning widely at her clumsy attempts to do likewise, watching her with quiet amusement as she struggled on long after he had finished.

'Tell me about your family,' he asked without warning as they drank delicious coffee. 'I know nothing about you.'

'My mother is an ordinary woman. We live in an ordinary house,' she said with cautious brevity, hastily trying to work out if this would give him any sort of advantage.

'And your father?' he asked, leaning back and watching her lazily.

'I've no idea,' she informed him flatly. 'He walked out, long before I was born.' Surprisingly, he said nothing, and after a second she looked up accusingly. 'I didn't tell you that to gain any advantage,' she stressed, trying to read the expression in his eyes. 'I can cope with life without sympathy and I don't even know him. What you've never had, you can't miss.'

'I'm not in the least sympathetic, *signorina*,' he assured her with raised eyebrows, obviously startled that she should imagine that he could feel sympathy and related foolish emotions. 'I'm not inclined to give you any advantages; I'm playing to win. As to not missing something you've never had, I disagree. Otherwise I would not be so eager for victory.'

He had paid the bill and led her back into the sunshine before she decided that all the remarks running through her head had better be left there. She treated him with disdainful silence, which perturbed him not at all.

The flower lady called to him as they passed by on their way back to the office and, after a quick exchange of words that left the jolly-looking little creature grinning toothlessly, Nick tossed her a coin and selected a long-stemmed red rose, which he presented to Rachel with a Latin flourish.

'I don't want . . .' she began heatedly, but he silenced her easily.

'Let us not go down that particularly slippery road again, *signorina*,' he advised, 'or I may have to show you that you do. A rose, however, is reasonably innocuous and I did not buy up the whole basket of flowers. Come, accept it graciously. You are merely required to carry it, not place it between your teeth.'

He suddenly had her giggling and she did not feel nearly so conspicuous as he took her arm, but walked along quite happily, the rose in her other hand. At least he was taking an interest. Maybe now he would ask her out at night. Then she could begin to use her stick.

He did not, however, ask her out; he was much too subtle for that. Instead, he continued to ignore her and now, securely trapped with her back to the office complex and no excuse to turn herself around, she couldn't even flutter her eyes at him.

On Thursday, though, half an hour after she had got back to her flat, a messenger arrived with one red rose. There was no message but she had no doubt that Nick had sent it. Her immediate inclination was to send it back, but on second thoughts, she kept it, placing it in the narrow vase in the sitting-room with the one from the previous day.

After a few days she needed a bigger vase because with determined regularity, Saturday and Sunday included, the messenger arrived bearing one new red rose each day. By the following weekend she was heading towards a full vase and Nick Orsiani had not spoken to her once. The original rose was now looking a little jaded but she was oddly reluctant to throw it out, telling herself that when she knew what he was up to she would throw the lot out together.

On the second Saturday, the messenger never came. She waited, watching the clock, strangely and childishly disappointed that this contact had been withdrawn, feeling quite unexpectedly lonely, as if she was cut off from all contact with the outside world because the grey-eyed Italian had forgotten to send a rose or had tired of it.

Exactly one hour later, just as she had washed her hair and tied it in a towel, the doorbell rang and her heart gave a peculiar leap as she thought that perhaps he had not forgotten after all; maybe there had been some hold-up at the florist. She rushed to open the door in her dressing-gown, leaving the shower running, ready to grab the rose and dive back under the warm water.

But when she opened the door, Nick Orsiani stood outside, tall and immaculately dressed, carrying the Saturday rose.

'Had I known that you greeted the messenger so eagerly, looking like that,' he remarked softly, 'I would have brought each rose myself.'

He walked in uninvited and she stood staring at him foolishly, her mind telling her to order him out, her femininity wanting her to hide because she looked such a mess, and her cunning telling her that this was what she wanted, a personal visit.

'We are going out for the evening,' he announced calmly, walking over to the vase and putting the new rose into it, obviously noting, but making no comment about the fact, that they were all there, even the first wilting bloom.

'My—my hair's wet,' she stammered, beginning to

feel very annoyed that he had caught her off guard. She didn't look too alluring at that moment, wet hair tightly pulled into a towel, bare feet, anxious hands clutching her dressing-gown around her.

'I will wait until you dry it,' he stated, turning and sitting down, clearly intending to stay there until she was ready.

Once again, with the silver-grey eyes on her, she had the ridiculous urge to back out of the room, only more so now, aware as she was of her scant covering, equally aware of his eyes that were beginning to roam over her. She dived towards the shower, slamming the bedroom door, feeling clumsy, gauche and uneasy. There was also a rising excitement that she knew must be the thrill of her success in getting him to take a personal interest at last.

'Where are we going?' she asked warily as they began to leave the city, the car steadily climbing as the sun began to set.

'It is a little too early for dinner yet and, while there is still good light, I want to show you something.'

'What?' she asked, trying to keep the anxiety from her voice, hoping that it wasn't his flat. She hadn't worked herself up to that yet; that would be the final strike.

'I want to show you something that belongs to me,' he said quietly, a softness in his voice that she didn't understand. 'It is a hill,' he finished and said nothing more.

CHAPTER FOUR

NICK stopped the car on a wooded track, still close to the city but seemingly miles away. There was stillness, and when he helped her from the car she stood listening, the wind blowing softly against her, moulding her dress to her body, blowing the rich and beautiful hair around her finely boned face.

'It's quiet.' Rachel looked up. He was watching her intently, his eyes on the slender outline of her figure, her creamy face, and she blushed softly as she realised that there was a kind of hunger in the way he was watching her, a fascination in the depths of the grey eyes.

'Is this it, then?' she asked with an attempt at nonchalance, baffled that the look on his face didn't infuriate her. Instead, it only made her heart pound and she was grateful when he smiled and held out his hand, breaking the spell that was becoming too uncomfortable to be managed.

'No, we are almost there but we can take the car no further. I should have told you to bring shoes with a lower heel,' he added regretfully, looking down at her slender-heeled shoes. 'However, if it is too rough we will leave it for another day.'

She suddenly didn't want to leave anything for another day; she just wanted this day to go on as it was doing and she put her hand in the hand that reached to help her with no hesitation.

'Up here,' he pointed out and they began to climb the rising ground that looked over the city.

'Rome, as you probably know, was built on seven hills,' he remarked as they climbed. 'There is very little ground left now to build even a hut, but this belongs to me.'

He spun her round as they came to the crest of the hill and she stood enthralled at the view of the city that lay below them. The wind was warm and soft; lights were beginning to twinkle far away as night covered the lower slopes first, leaving them still in the dying sunlight, and she could see the stretch of hillside that he had called his own.

It was tree-clad and green, with natural rock outcrops in a few places, the land already looking terraced as if some long-ago farmer had worked hard on it. There had never been a building here, but there was a luxury of vegetation that was not all a haphazard blessing of nature. Already there were flowering bushes, the beginnings of a path and, towering over all, the dark green of cypress trees.

'It's beautiful!' she breathed in an awestricken voice. 'What are you going to do with it?'

'I intend, I think, to build a house. I have a luxurious flat in the city. My father has a house just off the coast on a small island there, but I have no house of my own and, at thirty-three, it occurs to me that perhaps I should have one. I have had this land for a long time. Once or twice I have been tempted to get rid of it, but I cannot live in a flat for ever and I cannot really leave Rome; there is too much work and responsibility for me to be far from the city.'

'It would be a wonderful place to have a house,' she said enthusiastically, forgetting every anger in her delight with the place, but he still looked doubtful.

'There are plenty of trees to clear,' he observed, looking around at the magnificent trees that topped the hill.

'No!' She almost grabbed him and shook him in her horror. 'You could build half-way down. You'd have a

wonderful backdrop of trees.' She moved further down
to assess the situation, looking up past him at the hillside.
'It could all be terraced. It's partly done already, can't
you see?' She suddenly stopped, laughing self-con-
sciously as he stood watching her. 'Sorry, I'm getting
carried away.'

'No. I brought you here to ask your opinion. I know
that you never hesitate to speak your mind and you're
quite right.'

He walked further down the hill, standing to look up
at the possible site, his eyes thoughtful, and she almost
forgot about him as her mind began to build a house:
long, low, white, with the trees behind it and the city
below it, terraced gardens reaching to the road.

'It is almost dark,' he suddenly said softly. 'We had
better find our way down while we still can.'

It saddened her, as if somebody had said that she
could not stay in a beautiful place any longer because she
was not needed there; she felt an outsider, lonely and
chastened. She turned quickly to walk down to him, too
quickly, and moved towards him with a speed that
would have had her falling headlong if he had not
reached out and caught her.

'You are so anxious to leave this place?' He laughed,
his arms still around her, his hands locked comfortably
against her back.

'No, I was just a little careless,' she said, her face
flushed in the evening light, her breathing oddly
difficult. She didn't move from the circle of strength
that held her and he didn't seem anxious that she should.
For a second they simply stood there and then she found
the courage to look up into his face, unexpectedly
discovering that his eyes held the same hungry look, the
same barely concealed desire.

'Don't look at me like—like that,' she found herself
whispering, still standing entranced, her face appealing

in the gathering darkness.

'How can I not?' he asked thickly, his arms tightening, his face tight and still. 'I have never pretended that I do not want you and it is over six weeks since I held you in my arms. I didn't bring you here for this; I brought you to show you my land, to see what your reaction was as a woman. I never expected that you would run into my arms. Now I can only be certain of my reactions as a man. I want to make love to you.'

He didn't pull her towards him roughly as her bewildered mind half expected; he bent slowly to her lips, almost tentative, as if questioning his right to presume so far, and Rachel supposed that it was this unexpected hesitation that made her move half-way towards him, her own caution drowned in a surging feeling of sweet pleasure as their lips met, tasted and met again.

He drew back and looked down at her, deeply searching her eyes, his own blazing into life at what he saw there, and then there was no hesitation, no diffidence. He pulled her against him, moulding her to him with long possessive strokes of his sensitive hands, claiming her mouth with heated eagerness, clasping her head in strong fingers and holding her fast, her lips fused with his.

It was so unexpected, so swift, that she stiffened with fright and, as he felt her reaction, he cradled her against him, tempering his desire to meet her fear, his mouth coaxing hers to life, his hands moving over her with tender persuasion until she softened and became a willing captive in his arms.

His lips became more demanding as the fire between them grew steadily until she was aware of nothing but the feverish desire of her own to cling to him. In those moments she forgot all the things she knew about him; her anger, her determination to shatter his great ego,

disappeared from her mind. She was only aware of her
own needs, needs that almost matched his because never
in her life before had she felt like this. Never had she felt
herself swept out of her depths by a great tide of
emotion. She never struggled to free her mind just as she
never struggled in his arms; it was beautiful, terrifying,
utterly overpowering, and she let herself go down in the
tide of it, drowning in painful sweetness.

'Rachel!' His husky voice penetrated the swirling
mists of passion that held her fast. 'Rachel, come with
me, come back to my flat, stay with me, sleep with me,
we are perfect together.'

It brought some measure of sanity to her to hear his
voice and she realised that she should have been grateful.
If he had decided to take her here and now she would
have had no resistance in her. She drew back, trembling
violently, her hands moving to cover her face, but he
pulled them away with fingers that were surprisingly
gentle.

'Don't try to hide from me,' he said thickly. 'Don't be
embarrassed and shy because you have felt the flames of
desire. It was inevitable from the moment we saw each
other.'

'I—I'm frightened,' she managed to whisper, grateful
that he pulled her back into his arms and simply held
her.

'I understand,' he said, his own voice unsteady. 'I
almost feel frightened myself. I've never actually felt
frenzied about anyone before. At this moment I can
think of nothing but possessing you, but we will get to
know each other better if you are afraid. There is plenty
of time. With fortitude, I can even last out a whole
week.'

Whether it was the rueful humour in his voice or
whether it was her own sudden feeling of guilt and
shame as she realised, now that the heat had fled, that

she had been a willing captive in his arms, equally
responsible for fuelling the fire, she did not know, but
her mindless response to him left her with a cold fear
that horrified her. She hated him! What was she doing
welcoming arms that claimed her as if he had every
right, listening to a man who was ruthless, urging her to
his bed? She was shocked and disgusted with herself,
but her mind was now wide awake and she had more
than her share of caution. He must not realise how she
felt, not here in this lonely place. For now, he was gentle,
treating her tenderly, sure that he had won and merely
had to wait. If he knew what was in her mind, he would
show no mercy and she had little doubt that, back in his
arms, her treacherous body would react with age-old
instinct. She kept silent and he took her silence to be a
sign of her fright and shyness.

On Monday morning, after a nerve-racking day, and
a near-sleepless night, Rachel was filled with thankful-
ness that her earlier anger had prompted her to place her
back to the office complex. She worked harder than she
had ever done in her life, trying to bury the feelings that
churned around inside, keeping up with any work that
Bill pushed at her with such speed that he looked at her
oddly and complained that he was beginning to feel
harassed. She could have told him that he felt not one bit
as harassed as she felt, but she was on her own in this.

An errand to another floor at the end of the working
day brought her back past Nick's office as a woman was
just entering. She was certainly a woman to draw
attention. Petite, blonde, her face astonishingly beautiful, her clothes expensive and tasteful, she drew Rachel's
eyes, too. She had a glimpse of Nick's look of happy
surprise, of him leaping up to embrace her, and then the
door closed. He never saw Rachel.

'She is something to stare at, yes?'

Rachel turned to find one of the managers watching

her, a smile of sympathy on his face. She recognised him
as the one Nick had spoken to the other day when they
had been on their way to lunch and it was very obvious
that he thought her mind was seething with jealousy
after he had noticed Nick's possessive hand on her that
time.

'Very beautiful,' Rachel commented briefly and
moved to go on her way.

'Stefanie Veccetti, *signorina*. To be perfectly correct,
Princess Veccetti.'

He looked amused when she stopped and stared, then
he shrugged in the manner that she had now come to
accept as normal here.

'There are lots of remnants of nobility in Italy. One
might almost say that they are scattered around the
country with a haphazard indiscrimination. Mostly they
never use the title and mostly they are as poor as the next
man, but Princess Veccetti is a very wealthy woman.'

'Well, thank you for the information,' Rachel said
with what she hoped was cool indifference. 'If I ever see
another princess in Italy, I'll keep your remarks in
mind.'

He laughed, looking more interested by the minute,
and she had the urge to back away rapidly as he
advanced. She had enough problems right at this
moment without an unwanted admirer, and his interest
was all too plain.

'I think that they are trying to keep the situation as
low-key as possible for the moment,' he said with low
conspiracy that necessitated moving closer. 'The marriage will have to be managed with skill and speed if the
shares of both firms are to remain stable. She owns a very
prosperous light aircraft factory, among other things
that her late husband left her, and there would be talk of
a merger if the situation got out. I think that Signor
Orsiani would be very annoyed if there was to be

speculation on the market with Orsiani Italia shares. However, we all understand. Here, we are discreet.'

'I can see that you would be,' Rachel said quickly, backing off, trying to keep the anger from her face. A forthcoming marriage with Pricess Veccetti was not stopping Nick Orsiani from trying to seduce one of the people who worked for him. It was like some sort of Victorian melodrama. She felt a burst of fury at his cool presumption, at his cold-blooded shattering of her plans. His plans were going ahead, discreetly and quietly, his wedding date no doubt fixed. Hers had been fixed, too, until he had stepped into her life with a ruthless determination to make her his mistress.

She was thankful that she had managed to keep a tight control over her feelings, to keep her face bland, because at that moment Nick's door opened and he showed his visitor out. He also saw Rachel and the look on the face of the Italian manager. The manager walked off rapidly but Rachel never got the chance.

'What did he want?' Nick was beside her, his hand on her arm, before the figure of Stefanie Veccetti had gone more than a few yards. 'What was he talking to you about?' he demanded harshly when she simply looked at him in astonishment.

'Nothing particularly,' she lied rapidly. 'He was telling me that there was a big meeting in the city tonight and there would be a lot of traffic hold-ups,' she invented easily, suddenly remembering the item of news that Bill had tossed her way during the course of the afternoon. 'I don't really need to know, not having a car.'

'We'll avoid it,' he promised, his tight shoulders relaxing. 'When I collect you for dinner we will go in the other direction.'

'No, thank you,' Rachel said coolly, looking straight at him, trying to balance in her mind the sudden and inexplicable feeling of pain that came to her when his face lost its look of relief and showed bewilderment, and the satisfaction she felt at her ability to strike out at him as he deserved.

'What do you mean by that strange remark?' he asked with quiet care.

'I mean, Mr Orsiani, that I will not be going out to dinner with you, or anywhere else for that matter.'

She was in his office, the door closed and Nick towering over her before she could draw breath, and for a second he stood in an attitude that radiated menace, looking down at her with angry grey eyes. Then he moved away to lean against his desk, his legs stretched out in front of him, his long brown fingers loosening the top button of his shirt, pulling his tie away from its smart, exact positioning as if he was slowly trying to ease the tension and control his anger.

'Last night, Rachel,' he said with an almost weary sound in his voice, 'you were in my arms, as fiercely licked by flame as I was. You were shivering with the same passion, thirsting with the same desire. Had I pursued the advantage that your ardent body gave me then, we would now be lovers, and don't bother to deny it,' he added, as she opened her mouth to do just that. 'We both know that it is true. Now,' he continued, his face hardening from weariness to anger, 'you call me Mr Orsiani as if we were strangers, and inform me that I do not wish to go anywhere with me again. Last night you were as anxious as I that our destination should be my bed.'

He looked at her fiercely, his eyes cold and hard on her flushed face, his expression giving no quarter, determined to drive her into a corner, and she felt a rising anger inside her that added to the flush of embarrassment.

'The moment that I saw you, I knew what sort of a

man you were,' she snapped, almost choking with rage.
'And every day you go out of your way to prove me
correct. You've interfered in a life that is no concern of
yours—mine. My life! Now you stand here calmly
talking about your bed, when not more than a few
minutes ago I actually saw another woman in your arms!
How many beds do you have, Mr Orsiani? Or do you
plan to use the same one on a strictly rotational basis?'

For a second he looked stunned and then an
expression of deep wariness flitted across his face, to be
replaced almost at once by his normal sardonic and cold
gaze.

'I assume,' he said softly, 'that you are either once
again in the deep intrigue of your madly impossible
game, or that you have misunderstood a situation about
which you know absolutely nothing. I gather that you
are referring to Stefanie Veccetti?'

'Oh, do let us be quite correct,' she said sharply.
'Princess Veccetti. I do like things to be precise and in
order.'

'I think,' he suggested quietly, his grey eyes beginning to darken, 'that you are more than a little jealous. Is
that why you have resorted once again to your game of
evasion? If it is, I can tell you that ...'

'Don't bother!' she interrupted viciously, wildly
angry with both him and herself that the thought of the
petite blonde had bothered her in a way that she would
not have wished. 'I don't need to be told anything; I
understand you only too well. I am not playing any
game. I told you quite a few days ago that it had all been a
moment of anger and that there was no sort of game
between us. There is nothing between us, Mr Orsiani. I
asked you then to simply leave me alone. Even now, I
have no right to be in your private office, discussing
things that have no bearing on my work here.'

'And last night, Rachel?' he asked quietly. 'Last night

when you were afraid in my arms, afraid of your own desires?'

'I am not attempting to deny that last night happened,' she whispered, feeling without warning a sudden burst of deep pain inside at the memory of his arms around her. 'I am not entirely blaming you, either. I'm old enough to be responsible for my own actions and I found out that I am as vulnerable in your arms as any other woman is, I imagine. I don't suppose that my reaction was any surprise to you; you must have had that reaction plenty of times in your conquests.'

He said something in Italian that she was thankful not to understand, but by some supreme effort of will he remained where he was, though the look in his eyes was enough to make her thankful that he kept his distance.

'So, you felt nothing but a primitive sexual urge then, *signorina*?' he enquired sarcastically, 'and I have the ability to arouse in you a feeling that frightens you into flight?' He was staring at her coldly and she knew that she had to get out of there fast, even if her only method of doing it would probably lead to violence on his part. 'The way you were in my arms last night makes me doubt my wisdom in sending Pearson to Zarein. If he is willing to give up all that fire to go to somewhere that is merely hot, then I begin to wonder if he is mentally stable!'

'Chris is not like you!' Rachel flared, taking the line he had inadvertently given her in order to escape. 'He never behaves like that. He hasn't got your great masculine ego and he doesn't need to be surrounded by women to assure him that all is well in the world. You told me that there were people in the streets of Rome who were predators; well, I think that there's one here, too. In future, Mr Orsiani, I would be pleased if you would remember that I am an employee and that you employ me. There is nothing more between us than that. If you are not able to continue to remember that, then I shall break my contract and pay my own fare back to England!'

'Stop this damned game, Rachel!' he rasped, his voice rising in temper. 'Whatever you say, whatever you do, I know that you want me, and I want you too much to go on fencing warily around you.'

'I have said all that I intend to say,' Rachel informed him, the memory of the Italian woman that he intended to marry uppermost in her mind. 'Play your crude masculine games with some other secretary. Sooner or later, Princess Veccetti will find out, if she doesn't suspect it already. Still, I imagine she knows what to expect and can handle it easily. After all, she's one of your own class, not a lowly secretary like me. Somebody once said that morals are for the working-class, and I know where I stand. It's not always possible to have everything that one wants; you should have been taught that when you were much younger. Perhaps your hands should have been slapped when you were reaching for the cake.'

For a second, he stared at her, his face pale and tight with anger, and then he nodded slowly, straightening up from the desk.

'So you are slapping them now?' he enquired in a low, controlled voice. 'Reminding me also of what I said to you when I was angry, angry because you had made me so. You do not speak my language,' he continued in a vibrant voice, 'but you have a masterly control of your own language. Your tongue is capable of dripping poison and you have little regard for the accuracy of the words that fly from your lips.' He turned away, his back to her, his hands thrust deep into his pockets. 'Very well, you have painted a picture of great clarity in well-chosen words. I employ you and nothing more. In that case, *signorina*, get out!'

She went, as quickly and quietly as she could, glancing anxiously at her watch and finding with trembling relief that it was time to finish, hurrying along to snatch her bag and hasten past his office on her way out of the building.

She had done everything that she had wanted to do, reduced him to the level that he should be kept at, and dented if not demolished his inflated ego. She had compared him verbally with Chris and found him wanting, as far as he knew, and she should be gleefully pleased with herself. So she wondered unhappily why she was the one who was hurting inside. He was wildly angry, but she was curiously empty, suddenly very much alone.

She realised that since she had come to Italy she had not once thought of Chris and even now, when her angry and determined outburst had included his name, she could only hazily remember his face. If he had not really loved her then she had equally not loved him; it had merely been comfortable, easy, a habit.

She realised, too, that they should both be grateful to the clear-eyed Italian who had torn them ruthlessly apart, but gratitude was not what she felt. There was only an unending ache inside her when his face swam into her mind, a deep and stupid feeling of loss when she remembered the beautiful woman who had walked into his office, making his face light up with happiness. However much she despised him and all that he stood for, she could not shake off the other feelings.

Next morning, Bill informed her in another of his throwaway remarks that the big boss had left for Florence, and she was grateful for that. She could not face him yet; she had to bolster up her courage first. But Nick was temporarily wiped from her mind when, later, she looked up to find an almost forgotten figure standing looking at her as she bent over her notes.

'My dear little Rachel, the gentle rescuer of foolish foreigners, the little lady with hair like a flame and a kindly heart.' It was Vincenzo Orsiani, Nick's father, his eyes as dark as Nick's were pale, his face wreathed in smiles as he stood watching her, and her own smile was one of pleasure and genuine gladness.

'You do not mind that I call you Rachel?' he asked easily, coming forward to kiss her hand graciously. 'I cannot be at all formal with someone who has seen me at my very worst.'

Bill Taylor stood in bewildered silence as they greeted each other and then the Italian turned to him with a wide and rueful grin.

'You remember, Signor Taylor, my visit to your country when we acquired your firm? That is when I became at my most vulnerable. Without the help of Rachel, I think I would have created an incident.'

Bill continued to look dumbfounded and Rachel supplied the answer that the mischievous little man was clearly not about to offer.

'The better part of a whole bottle of Scotch,' she explained, her own eyes dancing with amusement.

'Oh!' Bill's long drawn-out word and his look of surprised understanding had Vincenzo Orsiani in further depths of laughter.

'It was after the official dinner,' he explained, apparently still delighted by his own fall from grace. 'I had sampled the drink for the first time, surprisingly. I very much enjoyed it and, being capable of consuming Italian wine with no ill effects, I saw no reason to deny myself this nectar. Rachel noticed my erratic behaviour and came to my rescue. As I recall, she said, "Come along Mr Orsiani, let us get you to your room nicely." She was just like a little nursemaid with a silly boy. She saved my dignity, took off my jacket and my shoes, loosened my tie and urged me to my bed. Next day I found her asleep on the settee in my sitting-room. She had been afraid that I would arise in the night and injure myself. Luckily it was a Saturday. We were both able to go away and recover, I from a head that threatened to kill me and Rachel from a stiff neck. We kept the whole thing very quiet, did we not, Rachel?' He finished with a hearty laugh, throwing one arm around her and giving her a huge hug.

Their laughter was stilled as an angry-faced Nick suddenly appeared in the entrance to Bill's office, his face tightening even more when he saw Rachel's smiling face and his father's arm securely around her.

'So, here you are,' he growled, his eyes avoiding Rachel's with no effort at all. 'They told me that you had arrived.'

'They told me, too, that you were in Florence,' Vincenzo Orsiani said with a quick anxiety that was lost on both Bill and Rachel.

'I have just returned and you had better come along; Stefanie came with me. We now have a good chance to talk things out and make a few plans. I cannot spare the time to come to the villa.'

'Good. I will come now,' his father said with a little sigh of relief. 'I have done what I wanted to do; I have renewed my acquaintance with the delightful Rachel.' He gave her a last hug of gratitude and affection and Nick's dark face darkened even further.

'Then if you have quite finished, let us get on,' he said tersely, walking out.

It was all a surprise to Bill, although he said nothing, but it was crystal clear to Rachel. With his father here, Nick wanted the wedding plans discussed. His stay in Florence had been with Princess Veccetti. She wondered with a wild sort of pain where Nick had slept, her imagination feverishly seeing the beautiful and petite Italian in Nick's powerful arms.

She returned to her work with a vicious speed that had Bill looking at her askance, wondering why she was not recounting to him the details of the tale that Vincenzo Orsiani had started, shrugging with a puzzled look and going back to his own desk when she never even looked up.

It was after lunch before she saw Nick's father again and once more he popped up like a merry little jack-in-the-box beside her desk.

'I am inviting you to my villa for this weekend, Rachel,' he said as soon as he had her attention, 'and I shall be hurt and very downcast if you refuse.'

'Oh, Mr Orsiani, I—I . . .' She could hardly say that she couldn't be near to Nick, that she didn't want to go somewhere where she would be reminded of him, but the smiling face opposite weakened her resolve to be merely an employee and keep the Orsiani family out of her life.

'It is on a little island just off the coast,' he coaxed. 'The sea is blue, clear and enticing. You could swim and improve the delightful tan you have acquired. And if you are thinking that your bad-tempered boss will be there,' he added astutely, 'you need not worry. Nick has already returned to Florence; at least, he is well on his way. He rarely finds time to visit me now, and there will be no one at the villa except you and I and my staff, unless of course my nephew Toni should arrive. I now see more of him than my son.'

He suddenly sounded a bit lonely and Rachel felt lonely herself. What did it matter? Soon, when the six months were up, she would be back in England and she would never see Nick again, never see this kindly little man whose ways were so different from his powerful son.

'How will I get there?' she asked with a smile that brought an answering smile to the soft brown eyes.

'I will drive you. I am leaving in one hour and I will get you the rest of the afternoon off. I heard Signor Taylor telling Nick that you were working like a fiend so I should think that there will be no protests there, he may even be glad to see you leave early. We will then take my boat out to the island. It is only a short way, just off the coast, south of Capua Baletti. You will need a bikini or two because, if you forget anything, there are no shops on the island, only my villa and miles of sand, and I know that young ladies do not like to be without the things that make life worth living.'

Rachel was happily excited. It was a chance to leave Rome, even if only for a couple of days, and it would take her mind off the fact that Nick Orsiani was back in Florence with his future wife. Her anger at his cool presumption had now turned to feelings that she refused to take out and examine, but she could not escape the fact that he was constantly on her mind, and his cold face when he had walked in and seen her with his father was still in her memory, too close to be dismissed easily.

During the drive to the coast, she managed to give all her attention to Nick's father and to the scenery of the places they passed through. He was a lively companion, an attractive man, and she remembered with a feeling of surprise how she had neatly written him off when she had been speaking to Cynthia. 'Plump, bald-headed and fatherly, sixty-five if he's a day.' It was quite laughable really. He was charming and easy to be with, nowhere near as old as she had remembered him, a mischief in the dark Italian eyes that would have turned many heads even now, and her amusement at her own dismissive attitude towards him kept a smile on her face that clearly pleased him.

They were sitting on the patio next morning, looking out over the blue sea, breakfast over and cleared by one of the servants who fussed continually over Vincenzo

Orsiani, when he suddenly lifted his head, listening.

'Nick,' he said with certainty, his eyes scanning the blue sky. 'I know the sound of that helicopter.'

'He flies a helicopter?' Rachel asked, stunned at the flutter of her heart.

'No one does it better, or with more terrifying flare,' his father said absently, his eyes still searching the cloudless sky. 'I wonder if he has brought Stefanie. We will soon know when he begins to come in. If she is with him she will not permit any antics.'

'Antics?' Rachel found herself asking breathlessly.

'There! There he is!' Vincenzo Orsiani suddenly called, taking her arm and pointing out over the sea. 'He is too high; she is not there.' He turned to smile at her, his disappointment that his future daughter-in-law was not with his son quickly hidden.

'Antics? Yes. He has been flying since he was fourteen, Rachel, and he has a skill that I have seen in no one else. At eighteen he was taking part in sea and mountain rescues that were too dangerous for my liking. He took on jobs that the normal rescue pilots refused because of the danger. It was then that I brought him into the firm early. I know he has had to work too hard and too soon, but the people who have disapproved of my decision to drive him deeply into the business so young do not realise that if I had not, he would probably be dead by now. I did not relish the idea that his daring and skill would leave him, at the very least, seriously maimed one day.'

She found herself staring upwards at the speck of darkness that the keen-eyed Italian had seen long before her, her mind trying to grasp the idea of Nick Orsiani as a young man with no fear, flying close into mountains, riding gigantic waves. It was an idea that came readily when she thought about Nick.

'No, she is not with him. He will drop like a stone. You

had better get a grip on your nerves, my dear Rachel,'
Vincenzo Orsiani said with a laugh.

'Do not get too anxious,' he added with further
laughter, 'he will not drop on us. It is his way of landing
when the devil is on his back. He will come in as near to
vertical as possible and he will land on that small square
of lawn and infuriate my gardener.'

Now that she could see the helicopter, a small and
unlikely bird in the clear blue of the sky, Rachel could
not take her eyes from it. It seemed from this distance to
be completely still, so far up that there was only the faint
sound of an engine, but she knew who was there and her
heart lurched sickeningly when, without warning, he
began to fall.

She had known helicopters for many years, seen them
made and seen them flown, and she could see what
Vincenzo Orsiani meant when he had said that Nick was
in a class of his own. It flashed through her mind that
Chris had said that he had made Nick uneasy. It was
laughable! He was simply falling out of the sky, turning
and falling as if he was a man in a rage, pushing the
machine to the very limit of its capabilities, courting
death with angry delight.

Within seconds, it seemed, the thundering of the
whirring blades was directly overhead and she could see
Nick, a white helmet over his dark head, his face stark
and tight, a black shirt with rolled-up sleeves covering
the powerful arms that held the controls, strong legs in
black jeans, a grim-faced opponent to battle with the
devil.

He hovered over the brilliantly green lawn, spinning
the machine in a last raging battle, the downward blast
of air bending the plants and bushes near to horizontal,
and Rachel heard Vincenzo Orsiani mutter angrily in his
own language. Then the machine touched the earth
delicately as a feather with a precise and masterly control

that brought a laugh of admiration to his father's lips.

'The devil has landed,' he observed quietly and she had to agree that, at that moment, Nick looked more like the devil himself than a man who had fought with darkness on the way down.

'Telephone, *signore*!' The call from the open doorway of the villa had Vincenzo Orsiani hurrying off inside, leaving Rachel to face Nick alone, her heart hammering in her chest as she saw him swing from the machine, tossing the helmet on to the seat, his tall, lean frame halting in obvious shock and rising anger as he saw her.

Striding up the marble steps to the patio, he towered over her, everything about him registering rage.

'What are you doing here?' he demanded harshly. 'I understood that as an employee with me as your employer you were reasonably content. It is not the normal thing to come to one's home and discover that a mere employee is settled cosily in close confines with one's father!'

'He—he invited me and ...' Rachel began, her face pale and worried. She couldn't battle with Nick and let his father know the true state of affairs between them. Vincenzo Orsiani would be furious with Nick and disgusted with her. He had clearly been looking forward to the arrival of his future daughter-in-law, and the realisation that Nick was pursuing one of his employees at the same time would be very distasteful to him.

'He invited you and you gladly accepted,' Nick finished for her in a rasping voice. 'I have often heard him sing the praises of the red-headed angel who rescued him when he was in England. Is this why you were willing to come to Italy? You are now here to collect your reward? Has he set a monetary value on it?'

'I won't argue with you,' she whispered, turning away. 'I won't have him upset.'

'How very touching!' He spun her round, his fingers

biting into her shoulders, his eyes glittering coldly into hers. 'He softens your heart, *signorina*? Were you comforting him last night? Is that why, he brought you here? Or would your proper little mind draw the line at that? I am greatly surprised that you agreed to come at all, aware as you are of your position as a mere employee and aware, too, that I may have arrived at any time, bringing Stefanie with me. Your position would have been one of real embarrassment then, would it not? Or does your refusal to upset my father not stretch that far? Stefanie would have been very puzzled as to who you were being pursued by, my father or me!'

He suddenly let her go and strode off into the house. He had almost thrust her from him in disgust and she was left shaking with fear and confusion, a deep ache inside her that was growing steadily, fighting down tears that threatened unexpectedly. He could not have stated more plainly that Stefanie Veccetti was a permanent part of his life, yet he saw no reason to deny himself a mistress. She felt that she was drowning in humiliation.

CHAPTER FIVE

IT was a good while before his father came back, and
Rachel had time to regain control of her feelings, time to
stifle the deep and sudden hurt that Nick's insinuations
had driven into her. There was no sign of Nick, and his
father was cheerful, even though the helicopter had not
brought Stefanie Veccetti. He had clearly got over his
disappointment that his future daughter-in-law was not
to be a guest for the weekend.

Nick came back, too, after a while, now dressed in
white shorts, a deep blue sports shirt open and revealing
his strong tanned chest, and Rachel looked hastily away,
conscious of the quickening beat of her own heart at the
sight of his lean, aggressively masculine body.

'I'm going to windsurf,' he announced shortly to his
father. 'I'll see you in about two hours.' Vincenzo
Orsiani nodded and leaned back comfortably in his
chair, his eyes closed against the brightness of the sun.
Nick stood looking down at Rachel, his face cold and
still, the wildness of his temper now clearly under
control. 'Do you windsurf, *signorina*?' he scared her by
asking.

'No—er, no. I've never tried it. It looks hard.' She
looked away but he never moved and his next words
made her stare up at him in astonishment.

'If you brought a swimsuit, put it on; I will teach you
to windsurf.'

She got no chance to deny him this little cruelty
because his father sat up in enthusiastic agreement.

'A very good idea! Run along, Rachel dear, and enjoy

83

yourself. I've got a few telephone calls to make and I don't want to leave you to yourself.'

'I'll be perfectly happy just sitting here,' Rachel said hastily, but he was insistent, and Nick simply stood there waiting, everything about him saying clearly that he had no intention of going mildly away and leaving his father to the mercy of someone like her.

In the end, she had to agree, if only not to arouse his father's suspicions that Nick was in any way interested in her. She was back in minutes, her white bikini hidden beneath the thick folds of a beach robe.

He was waiting with a variety of equipment, towels, suntan lotion, cool drinks, and he pushed a life-jacket into her hands.

'Carry that, *signorina*,' he ordered. 'You can put it on before you go into the water.'

'I swim very strongly,' she protested but he refused to give ground.

'So does a fish,' he remarked evenly, 'but not nearly so well when he has received a blow on the head. You are attempting a new sport in fairly deep water. No life-jacket, no windsurfing.'

It was a good chance to refuse, but one look at his face stilled any thought of rebellion.

'Very well.' Ungraciously, with an air of defiance that brought a laugh from the older man and a quick glare from Nick, she took the offending garment and walked off down the steps to the beach.

If she had expected Nick's eyes to gleam with anticipation at the sight of her in her scanty covering, she would have been disappointed. He ignored her. His own clothes were tossed on to the huge beach towel, leaving him in a brief black swimsuit that had her hastily looking away, but his own eyes were only on the sea.

He left her standing irresolute as he assembled the sail

and dragged the now rather alarming contraption into
the surf. Rachel, ankle deep in the waves, watched with
widening eyes as he checked the whole thing
thoroughly.

'All right.' He looked across at her grimly, nodding
towards the dancing little craft, and she waded across to
him with great misgivings, knowing that he would be
happy to see her drowned or severely knocked about by
the blue and white sail. She didn't even know how to get
on to the pitching board.

He had no doubts, however. As she came within reach
he curved his arm round her waist, scooping her out of
the water and placing her effortlessly on to the board.
Even with one arm holding the little board in place, he
had no trouble in setting her on her feet and holding her
until she was balanced.

She expected a push, or simply to be allowed to drift
away and be tossed into the surf but, seeing the pitch of
the board, the rise of the waves, he sprang up beside her,
his brown arms trapping her firmly, and he uttered not
one word.

They seemed to be on the water for hours and, after
the first few frightening minutes, Rachel was filled with
an exhilarating excitement. The breeze whipped up
colour into her face, the sun was hot on her arms and she
felt free, safe, happy.

She knew that it was due entirely to Nick's skill. It was
his weight that balanced the light float, his strong arms
that skilfully tacked and steadied the sail. He was close,
but the life-jacket kept her free of contact with him and
his only comments were orders and encouragement.

On a few occasions, she was allowed to manoeuvre the
sail herself, his hands coming quietly to correct it when
she made any mistake, then after a while he took her
back to the beach.

'Now you may try on your own,' he shouted into her ear above the noise of the surf. 'Keep your balance and move with the wind. You are in shallow water here, nothing to worry about.'

The year's most masterly understatement, Rachel thought as she fell off for the eighth time, landing each time in increasingly ungainly positions, her arms aching with the effort to right the sail and drag it from the water.

'Enough!' Nick was beside her on her last undignified fall, pulling her to her feet, capturing the capsized craft and dragging it on to the sand.

'It's not easy,' she gasped, collapsing on to the beach towel, lying on her back, her breathing still jerky. For a second she forgot that he was hating her; it only seemed right to be with him, talking normally, but a look up at him had her changing her mind. His face was hard and cold.

'It takes practice,' he said briefly, tossing her a towel. 'You have had enough for one day, more than enough. I expected you to give up much sooner. Left to yourself you would have gone on struggling until you collapsed.' She could see that she was very stupid, his glance of annoyance told her so, and she was glad to bend over and begin to dry her hair, shutting him out of her sight. She didn't want to see his angry face any more.

When she looked up, he was already in the water again, the little craft under superb control, heading out into the bay. He had left her without a word and she stared at him until the blue and white sail became almost a speck on the blue water. He was a delight to watch, handling the board with ease and skill, almost flying across the water, tall and tanned and looking curiously free and lonely both at the same time.

For a while there had been a silent feeling of

companionship between them; even though he had not spoken, she had felt it. Now he was alone, back with his devils and his own thoughts, a man she neither understood nor trusted, a man she really knew nothing about, except that he was ruthless, savagely pursuing anything he wanted. He could make her feel things that she had never felt before in her life and at this moment she was frighteningly aware that she was in an alien land, at his mercy except for her ability to fight. There was no future with Nick Orsiani except to be degraded, and she had no doubts about his own future—Princess Veccetti!

She resolutely began to plan. The months would fly and then she would return to England and find another job, leaving Orsiani Italia and forgetting Nick Orsiani and her brief time in Rome. She lay on her stomach and closed her eyes, letting drowsy feelings wash over her, forgetting everything but the constant sound of the sea, the cry of the gulls, the sun hot on her skin. She was tired, too sleepy to care any more about anything.

The touch of a cool hand stirred her into partial wakefulness and she roused herself unwillingly.

'Rachel.' Nick's voice was close and for a few minutes she didn't know where she was. 'You'll be burned. Turn over. The sun is hot on your shoulders and you're probably burned already. You should never go to sleep in the sunlight. You do the most stupid things!' he added irritably.

She sat up sleepily, feeling yet again that she had behaved like an idiot, turning her face away from him and trying to bring herself to complete wakefulness, but cringing away when she heard his quick mutter of exasperation.

'Sit up properly and I will rub some lotion into your shoulders and back,' he said crossly. 'You are really the last word in idiots.'

'I can do it myself!' she snapped, now firmly back in a world she understood, a world where Nick growled at her and she snapped back at him. He pushed her reaching hand away from the tube of lotion, jerking her back to her original position with no kindness or thought for his hands rough on her skin.

'Just sit still and behave yourself for once,' he growled. 'I expect that if you have caught the sun too badly I shall be the one to blame and my father will treat you as if you have been severely neglected!'

'I don't want you to do anything!' she cried, trying to pull away, stiffening at his next words.

'We have already established that, I think. You are an employee and I have to be content with Stefanie with no pleasure on the side. All the same, I am not prepared to see you burn, even though we are strangers who will never meet again once our paths have separated.'

It was perfectly true, exactly what she wanted, but the knowledge did nothing to ease the sharp stab of pain that his hard words brought. He had meant to silence her with the hardness of truth and he had succeeded. She was securely held and sat stiffly as he smoothed lotion on to her shoulders, his breathing angry and hostile.

'Pull your hair forward, unless you want to get it greasy,' he muttered in an impatient voice and she took her hair in two hands, pulling it on either side of her face, bending her head to keep away from the movement of his hands and the harsh sound of his voice, willing him to finish quickly and leave her to her own misery.

'Do you know how vulnerable you look like that?' he asked suddenly, his voice oddly vibrant. 'Like some stricken creature waiting for her fate.' She tensed as she heard the tone of his voice, expecting some further outburst, but instead his hands moulded the delicate bones of her shoulders and his lips moved to the vulnerable and tender base of her neck exposed by her bent head.

She leapt under his hands at the shock of feeling that raced through her as his mouth touched her skin, and he pulled her against the coolness of his chest, still damp from the sea, a low moan of pleasure escaping him as he traced the slender bones of her nape with the tip of his tongue.

'Tell me that you don't want this, Rachel,' he challenged as she melted against him, unable to resist the urge to be close. 'Tell me that you feel nothing, that you wish to be nothing to me.'

She couldn't answer, her body beginning to catch fire from the stroking hands and lips, beginning to twist against him, wanting to turn into his arms as he teased her relentlessly.

'Nick!' Her little gasp of panic as his fingers found and dealt with the catch of her bikini top brought a murmur of satisfaction from him.

'At last! At last I am Nick! At last you acknowledge with your lips that I exist, as your body has been acknowledging it since we met. I want to touch you as I wanted to touch you the moment that I saw you.'

He tossed aside the bikini top, his hands warm and possessive, cupping the breasts that surged into them, his face in her hair as her body sprang to excited life. For long pleasurable seconds he stroked her until her face turned up to his of her own volition, looking into the darkened eyes that locked with hers as he turned her, placing her on the towel, his eyes devouring her as his hands swept over her with the right of possession.

'Tall and slender and lovely,' he whispered thickly, 'with hair like flame and a fire that burns almost to match my own. I want you, Rachel, and you want me.'

He lay beside her, pulling her into his arms, his hands moulding her to him with fierce urgency as her legs twined with his and her body melted against him, fitting with a perfection that spoke of her desire. She could feel the frenzy in him that he had confessed on the lonely hillside; his body was tense with a barely controlled passion, wanting to take her there and then, impatient with the necessity to remain in control.

And the same feelings raged through her and had her moving restlessly in his arms, straining to be yet closer, little whimpers of desire moaned against his face until he drew back and looked into her eyes, his own blazing with heat. The lips that captured hers were blazing, too, sending shock waves of pleasure through her until she was trembling uncontrollably, shaking in his arms, her breath coming in painful gasps when he allowed her air to breath.

With a sensuous murmur of pleasure, he bent his head and caught the rosy peak of her breast in his white teeth, shocking her into a little cry before soothing her with warm lips that nuzzled against her. It was as if the weeks of waiting had driven him beyond endurance, and his hands were harshly male and thrilling against her skin, his mouth insistent and demanding against her breast until she was arched against him, her whole body aware and alive, utterly responsive and vulnerable against the hard masculine force that moved against her, dominating her physically and mentally.

'Nick!' The feelings inside her were a real physical pain, a pain that instinct told her only one thing could erase, and at her demanding cry he raised eyes to hers that were filled with hunger, his hand heavy and restless on the smooth planes of her stomach.

'Not here,' he whispered huskily, an unquenchable fire in his face. 'Now you will be with me whatever anyone thinks. When I possess you it will not be over in a moment of passion; it will last until my soaring desire for you is satisfied, until we are too tired to touch each other, too tired to kiss.'

There was a finality in his voice, a hard compulsion that left no room for doubt as to her destiny. His voice was determined, impassive, harshly sure of her, and she found her mind running over his words like someone in a trance as he sat her up and helped her into her bikini bra. 'Now you will be with me whatever anyone thinks.' Who could he possibly mean but Stefanie? Nothing was any different in spite of his passion; he intended to continue as he had stated so clearly before. He needed only a mistress and he had set his desires on her; his real future was already settled. 'It will last until my soaring desire for you is satisfied.' She could almost end that little statement herself . . . 'and then I'll get on with my real life and you can go back to England.' The woman in his life was wealthy and titled, a woman of his world, and the reality of her situation gnawed away at her like a wound as she turned her face away when he would have kissed her.

'Rachel?' There was a thread of anxiety in his voice and she stood quickly, looking down at him, seeing the anxiety slowly erasing the passion from his face. 'Something that I have said has hurt you,' he said with an astute assessment of the look on her face. 'Or I have frightened you with my ardour. Rachel, I would never hurt you.'

'You won't get the chance,' she said calmly, every word like a knife inside her, 'because I'm just not interested.'

'The hell you're not!' he rasped violently, beginning to get to his feet. 'I'm beyond playing games with you, Rachel. You want me as much as I want you!'

'No!' she shouted, her mind trying to reject the truth. 'I wanted Chris! I wanted to get married to someone I had loved for years. You stepped uninvited into my life and I swore that I'd make you pay. Well, you're paying now, Mr Orsiani. You may want me but I'm glad to tell you that you're stuck with the beautiful Stefanie. If you need a mistress on the side, find another fool!'

'What the hell has Stefanie got to do with the way we feel?' he grated viciously, grasping her arm, towering over her.

'The way you feel,' she corrected.

Before he could stop her, before his look of utter disbelief had left him, she ran to the sea, wading out to the deeper water and striking out with powerful overarm strokes into the blue bay. Her heart was breaking inside her as realisation of her true feelings for Nick Orsiani overwhelmed her, and she swam without thought.

There was no consciousness of what she did; she simply swam, only stopping when her arms refused to make any more strokes. She had told the truth when she had said that she was a strong swimmer but the time on the float, the time in the sun and the ferocity of her feelings for Nick had left her strangely weak, lethargic. As she trod water and moved on to her back, she looked towards the far away shoreline and her mind admitted that she would never make it back to safety.

Nick's dark head surfacing beside her gave her a momentary shock as she looked across at him, but he wasted no time in useless talk. He dived and came up behind her, taking her in a powerful grip, saving his breath for the long haul to the beach, his strong legs cutting through the water, athletic and certain, his arms towing her along, one hand under her chin, until she felt the sand against her heels. He pulled her to her feet, dragging her through the surf and dumping her unceremoniously on the beach.

For a few minutes he said nothing, his head down, his breathing harsh and pain-filled, his hands on the strong bones of his hips, and then he turned on her eyes that were like icy wastes.

'Now I know!' he grated. 'Now I know with a certainty that will not be forgotten. You love this unfaithful boy who prefers adventure and a possible fame. You have lived your life in Rome with no other thought than to punish me, to get even. Words would have done! You have a fine command of those. There have been other women in my life who have not wanted me but you are the first who has felt the need to point it out by attempting to drown yourself! I will leave you here on the beach in safety, *signorina* and there will be no necessity to fling yourself back into the water. I have your message. I am to stick to Stefanie and leave you well alone. In future, we meet as strangers!'

He strode along the beach, dragging the sail and the float to the base of the cliff with an ease that spoke of fury, scooping up his shirt and shorts from the beach towel and climbing the steps to the villa two at a time while Rachel watched him with a deep pain inside, tears running down her face in never-ending streams.

It was along time before she could bring herself to go back to the house, to fix on her face a smile for Nick's father, and she dreaded meeting Nick. Her climb up the steps, however, brought her to the sunlit patio where the two men seated in the white and gold loungers did not include Nick. Vincenzo Orsiani was deep in conversation with another man, a younger man than Nick, with curly black hair and eyes as dark as Nick's were pale. There was the same mischief in the depths of the newcomer's eyes that lurked in the eyes of the older Orsiani.

'Rachel,' Vincenzo Orsiani called as she stepped into view. 'I had begun to worry about you. Nick has been back for a good while.'

'I stayed to sunbathe,' Rachel said quickly, wondering how this information would be received. Nick made little attempt ever to disguise his annoyance and now he was probably in a rage to end all rages. His father, however, took it calmly, only waving her across to join him.

'I live in fear, Uncle Vincenzo that you intend to refuse to introduce me to the *signorina*,' the smiling newcomer said, looking with interest at Rachel and getting an amused glance from his uncle.

'You are well aware that this is Rachel,' he said with chuckle. 'What you mean is that I am to bring you to Rachel's attention. My nephew, Rachel. Toni Orsiani, my late brother's son.' He smiled at her quick look of surprise. 'Do not worry, my dear, there is not an unending supply of Orsianis. Toni is the last one, until Nick marries and produces more.'

Rachel's sudden pallor at the mention of Nick's marriage went unnoticed as Toni took her hand and raised it gallantly to his lips. 'Or until I marry,' he commented, glancing in amusement at his uncle. 'There are a variety of possible sources for renewing the dwindling ranks, I think.'

There seemed to be an undercurrent of meaning in his words and Nick's father was saved from any reply as Nick suddenly appeared in the doorway of the villa and called to him. He was once again dressed in the outfit that he had arrived in and Rachel looked hastily away, one part of her hoping that he would now leave, another

treacherous part of her wanting to see him for much
longer.

'It is with great relief that I meet you, *signorina*,' Toni
said with a disarming smile as they were left alone. 'We
have heard about you for the last two years. Pardon me
when I say that my uncle has spoken of you so frequently
that your saintliness has become a conversation piece
that has driven us mad. You look very different from the
angel he described, I am happy to say. The gentle
creature who rescued my uncle when he was rolling
drunk, would not, I feel have had the nerve to windsurf
with the athlete of the family.'

'He wasn't rolling exactly,' Rachel laughed, glad to be
able to steer the conversation away from the subject of
Nick. 'He was a little disorientated.'

'I have seen him disorientated frequently,' Toni
assured her with a delighted laugh, his eyes as
mischievous as the dark eyes of Nick's father. 'He takes
life with a light-hearted attitude that Nick would do well
to copy. Nick works too hard; even his relaxation is
taken with a determined drive that is exhausting to
watch. One day he will simply drop in a burned out heap.
Even now he is apparently flying back to Rome; within
the week, I understand, he is going to Japan. However,
there is no arguing with Nick. He is the boss, as we all
know.'

'You work with Nick?' Rachel asked in surprise. She
had never in the office even heard Toni mentioned.

'For Nick,' Toni emphasised. 'I work in the factory at
the other side of the city. I run the place there, with
Nick's blessing and under his stern eye, I hasten to add.'

'I didn't know there was a factory in Rome,' Rachel
remarked in surprise. 'Nobody seemes to have mentioned it and somehow it never occurred to me.'

'You think that we live on paperwork, *signorina*?'

Toni queried, his head thrown back as he laughed. 'Surely you realise that we make helicopters and sell all over the world, besides our other products.'

'Of course I know,' Rachel laughed. 'It never occurred to me that the factory was near to Rome, though. I imagined that it was in some other part.'

'You are not used to the names, *signorina*. Perhaps you have not seen enough of my country? We will have to rectify that.'

He was leaning forward, watching her smiling face with a keen look of interest, when Nick appeared, turning to the steps that led to the lawn but halting and looking across at them. He turned an unsmiling face to Toni's pleasant farewell and spoke rapidly in Italian, his voice low, but incisive.

To Rachel's amazement, Toni looked embarrassed and as Nick strode down the steps and climbed into the helicopter, Toni said quietly, 'I'm sorry, *signorina*. I had no idea that my natural friendliness would bring his wrath in this direction.'

Rachel tore her eyes away from Nick, wanting to see him until the last possible minute but unable to ignore the rueful voice of his cousin.

'I'm sorry, I don't understand.'

'You do not speak Italian?' he asked with some surprise and, she suspected, some relief.

'No, I doubt if I ever will. What did you mean just then?'

'I was about to ask you to dine with me when we returned to the city,' he confessed with a wry grin. 'Luckily I had not got that far. Nick has just warned me off. You are to be left severely alone, *signorina*. I have been given the hands off signal, loudly and clearly. I'm sorry. I had no idea that you belonged to Nick.'

'I don't!' Rachel's gasp of surprise and embarrassment merely earned her a look of amused speculation from Nick's cousin and she turned her hot face towards the machine on the lawn to see Nick fastening his helmet, his dark face still and unreadable.

'I work for him,' she hastily added and then, as a rather unhappy afterthought, 'he probably only wanted to remind you that I am merely a secretary, of insignificant importance in Orsiani Italia.'

'Nick is many things,' his cousin said quietly, his eyes on her flushed face, 'but he is not and has never been what you would in England call, I believe, a snob. He worked his way through the firm as I have had to do, as Uncle Vincenzo did in his time. Nick has many friends of all types. Your—rank, *signorina*, has nothing to do with his sharp order to leave you alone. I can only assure you hastily that my intentions were wholly honourable. Even without Nick's intervention, I would hardly dare to upset my Uncle Vincenzo's ministering angel.'

The sudden deafening blast of the helicopter's engine had them both looking towards it as it rose slowly and vertically, making Rachel's heart sink as she thought that some other daring battle with the devil was to take place.

Instead, he rose to a height just over the roof top of the villa and then slowly circled, looking down on to the sunlit patio, his face clearly visible, watching them with a pointed menace that apparently was not lost on Toni.

He looked up and made a little seated bow of gracious defeat. 'There is no need to emphasise your point, my dear Nick,' he murmured as Nick moved away, to circle yet again. 'I expect to live a long and happy life, with your permission.'

Nick took off towards the coast with no further tricks, skimming low over the water like an angry wasp as Vincenzo Orsiani strode from the house.

'Why the hell did he do that, Toni?' he asked sharply. 'He's never done anything like that before. I expected the roof to come off, he was so low!'

'I think he was looking for something,' Toni suggested, tongue in cheek, his eyes on Rachel as she stared out to sea at the vanishing speck of angry sound that was Nick. Vincenzo Orsiani went back inside, muttering threats that he would soon forget and Rachel still watched seaward, her face unknowingly wistful.

'You're quite wrong,' she said softly, hardly aware that she spoke. 'He hates me actually, if you must know. When I've finished the six months in Rome, I intend to leave Orsiani Italia. Nick Orsiani is nothing to me and I am nothing to him. I've told you, I merely work for him.'

She turned back and her eyes met the keen dark gaze of Nick's cousin with a wan little smile.

'In that case, *signorina*,' he said with a wide grin, 'I would like now to invite you to dinner when we return to Rome. Shall we say Monday evening?'

'But—but I thought ...' Rachel began in alarm, silenced quickly by his wide grin.

'And you thought correctly, *signorina*,' he laughed. 'Let us say that I suddenly have a fancy to live dangerously. When Nick finds out, I will at least be in the company of a girl who has proved her nursing capabilities in this family. I imagine that you can also bathe wounds as well as protecting rolling drunks? You fancy a challenge?'

'Yes!' Rachel said, suddenly furious with Nick for the embarrassing situation she had been placed in, for the acute embarrassment he had caused his pleasant cousin. 'Yes I do! I look forward to having dinner with you on Monday!'

'I thought you would,' he smiled, his eyes on the red

flame of her hair. 'Please to remember though that I am on your side. I would not like to be attacked on two fronts. And now, Rachel, how would you like to swim again?'

'Very much,' she said determinedly, wishing that Nick could see his orders being ignored, smiling brilliantly at Toni when his eyes ran over her bikini-clad figure as she threw her robe on to the lounger. How dare Nick behave like that? How dare he warn off anyone else as if she was his property? In a few months' time he would probably be a married man, preparing to enlarge the Orsiani family. She stifled the stab of pain that the thought gave her and kept her smile fixed on her face as Toni rose indolently and turned to collect his swimming gear from the house, his eyebrows raised as he inspected her slender beauty again.

'How dangerously can you live?' he asked himself quietly with a slow grin that brought a quick flush to Rachel's face. 'At least I shall die happy.'

CHAPTER SIX

MONDAY morning at the main offices of Orsiani Italia had everyone scurrying round anxiously. Nick was leaving for his overseas trip and everyone knew it. They seemed to be praying almost to a man that the time would fly quickly to his departure, because this morning there was no doubt in anyone's mind as to who ruled Orsiani Italia and who was in the fury of a lifetime.

It was not that anyone suffered from the tidal wave of his wrath, but rather there was the air about him that led even the most insensitvie to realise that to cross him would probably be their last act in this life. Every manager was given personal instructions. He moved through the offices like a black whirlwind and when just before lunch he left for the airport, it seemed that the whole fabric of the building breathed out a sigh of relief.

At the very last minute, Rachel's own inclinations were to go to him and beg him to take care, because he seemed to be riding high on a wave of fury that would destroy him. But her courage would never have stretched that far and she knew that her reception would have been one of disdain. He had said that they would meet as strangers and he had meant it. They had passed during the morning and he had looked right through her. He had spoken to Bill a few yards from her desk and he had ignored her.

He had got her message, it seemed, and his sharp warning to Toni that she was to be left severely alone seemed to her to be only a means of cutting her off from any contact with the Orsiani family. Certainly it was not, could not be, for any other reason.

The evening brought the first of several outings with Toni. She left her flat with some misgivings now that her temper had subsided, but she returned after an enjoyable friendly evening with her heart a little lighter and Nick a little further into the back of her mind.

Not to far though. Toni, for example, had insisted on teaching her a few words of Italian, almost forcing her to learn them in his light-hearted, laughing way, and even this led her to feelings of guilt. Nick had promised to teach her, wanted to teach her. The fact that he had designated his bed as the learning ground was pushed into the back of her mind as she felt, foolishly, treacherous, as if in some obscure way she was hurting him. The very thing that she had set out to do.

She often wondered now who had been most hurt in the whole affair. Certainly not Chris. He was by now no doubt happily in control of his desert outpost, Beau Geste of the air. Nick had cut her from his life as cleanly as if with the sharp stroke of a knife and no doubt he was working with his usual speed and dedication in Japan, ringing Stefanie Veccetti in Florence to put the final touches to his wedding arrangements.

Forlornly Rachel realised that, as in the beginning, the hurt remained with her alone, and she went out almost every night with Toni, allowing herself to be engulfed in the present, smiling brilliantly, throwing herself enthusiastically into every outing, every visit to places of interest, until she felt like a star that had shone too long, too brightly, and was about to explode and burn out into nothing.

It seemed that Toni was determined to show her the place that he laughingly called his own private city. He was inordinately proud to be a Roman and there were clearly not enough hours in any evening for him to show her the wonders of Rome. From the Campidoglio Gardens with fine views of ancient Rome, to the two-

hundred-year-old Spanish Steps and to the Galleria
Borghese, she was taken on a seemingly unending tour
of Rome.

Her pleas to stop and linger by the chic shops in the
famous Via Condotti were determinedly ignored. It was
more important to view the bones of four thousand dead
monks arranged with macabre artistry in the crypt of
Santa Maria della Concezione or to view the Colosseum.

One place though was very special. Toni allowed
lingering and Rachel allowed her heart to rule her mind.

'The Fountain of Trevi,' Toni said softly one evening
as they approached the spectacular fountain, raising his
voice as they came closer to speak to her over the sound
of the cascading water. 'You know the legend, Rachel?
Toss in a coin and you will ensure your return to Rome.'

'I can't believe in things like that, I'm afraid,' she
laughed, suddenly deeply unhappy, smiling the more
brightly to hide her sadness. 'And in any case, I won't
even want to.'

He looked at her in silence for a long minute, his soft,
dark eyes seeing more than she would have wished, and
then he felt for a coin and handed it to her.

'*Per favore*,' he insisted when she shook her head in
smiling refusal. 'There is no way that we can tell from
day to day what tomorrow will bring. Perhaps a litle act
of faith will help tomorrow along.'

'I very much doubt it,' she said, looking away.
Nothing could help tomorrow along. Tomorrow, Nick
would be back; her wilful heart had counted the days
with a restless excitement and a deeper dread. But he still
held the coin out, saying nothing more, and she finally
took it, looking down at its glitter in her hand and then
tossing it into the glitter of the rushing water. She said
nothing as she watched it sink to join the others that lay
there, symbols of hope tossed in amusement or despair,
and her mind told her that it was just a coin, a game

played by a beautiful and famous kind of wishing-well.
But her heart repeated 'Nick' over and over until she
turned impatiently away, her eyes filled with tears.

This was the evening, too, when a growing uneasiness
became a reality. She had realised throughout the week
that, if she was not careful, there was a real danger of
Toni becoming deeply attached to her. From the first
they had been easy and comfortable in each other's
company and every time he met her his growing
pleasure at the meetings became more obvious. He was
charming, kind, and a good companion, more with the
character of his uncle than with any noticeable resem-
blance to Nick. The thought of hurting him in any way
was painful to her but, unless she stopped seeing him,
there was a chance that he would end up hurting, too.
He knew it, apparently, because as they stopped at her
flat he turned to her that night and made no move to get
out and escort her to her door.

'There is a confession that I must make to you and a
decision that must be taken now, tonight, Rachel,' he
said with an unusual seriousnes that brought an
unhappy sinking of her heart.

'What began as a joke, an act of defiance, has, I think,
backfired on me,' he continued quietly, his dark eyes on
her face. 'I wanted to take you out for both of us to enjoy
ourselves and to show Nick that I am not an underling to
be ordered about. Also, I must confess, your unhappy
face left me angry with Nick.'

He leaned across to her. 'We have enjoyed the time
together, have we not, Rachel?' he asked quietly, her
smiling agreement bringing an amused but rueful smile
to his own face. 'I have enjoyed it too much I think,' he
confessed quietly. 'If this continues, I will be prepared to
fight Nick for the right to be with you, to bring discord
to my family.'

'I'm sorry, I never meant anything to ...' Rachel

began but he stopped her, his hand coming to cover her own.

'I know. You, like me, were annoyed with Nick.' He shrugged in wry amusement. 'It is very easy to be annoyed with Nick and if I thought that there was even half a chance, then I would not care. You like me, I know, and I am prepared to leave it at that because I cannot see any point in hoping for more. Your heart is with Nick, yes?'

'No!' It seemed that only a loud and fierce denial to Toni would enable her to keep her feelings locked away from herself. 'Nick and I . . . You don't understand . . .'

'I do not need to, ' he assured her quietly. 'Nick treats me often as if I were a boy, but that is because of the responsibility he carries and refuses to share, because of the dangerous drive that rules his life. If he looked closely, he would see that I, too, am a man and as a man I see what is in your eyes, in spite of your desire to emulate Nick and throw yourself into a frenzy of enjoyment in order to cut him from your mind.'

She wanted to put her hands over her ears, to refuse to listen, to shout loudly in order to drive from her own mind the growing realisation of the truth of his quiet words. She never answered because there was no answer to give and he sighed in defeat, opening the door and coming round to help her out.

'Whether it is because I have heard so much about you for so long from my uncle, or whether it is your unusual slender beauty, or whether I am just like any other man, suddenly ensnared, I do not know. One thing I do know, Rachel, our outings must stop from this moment, I would, I think, fight Nick for you, but I cannot fight you. You understand?'

'Yes.' She looked at him sadly and he gave his usual grin.

'Do not take on any further grief,' he advised. 'I am

blessed with a tremendous ability to recover and I am pulling back before my feet become firmly lodged in the quicksand. *Arrivederci*, Rachel,' he added softly, leaning forward to kiss her cheeks. 'At least an early parting means that we will always meet as friends.'

She watched him drive away and then went sadly into her flat. His final words were so different from Nick's. She and Nick would always meet as strangers. She went to bed unhappily, beginning to realise that sorting out desire from love was not easy and brought too many heartaches. She would have been better married to Chris, living an ordinary life, raising his children and growing into secure middle age. She would never have known the frantic rapture of Nick's lovemaking, the determined desire of her body to defy her mind and belong to him; she would have been quietly content.

Her own words to Nick came back to her, 'What you've never had, you can't miss,' and she realised that it was far too late. She had been in Nick's arms, had felt the fire; it would take a long time to forget, perhaps as long as the rest of her life.

For only the second time in many years she cried herself to sleep, realising even in the depths of her misery that her tears for Chris had been almost wholly tears of embarrassment that soon everyone would know that Chris was happy to leave her. Now, she didn't care. Now, no other person entered her mind. She was crying for Nick, bitterly and heartbrokenly, refusing to face any other thought but that. She wanted him, needed him, longed for his smile, his protection, his love.

Whether in fact Nick had returned from Japan the next morning, nobody seemed to know. After a flurry of questions, everybody trying to squeeze information from other people who were equally in the dark, the day continued in pretty much the same way as usual and

Rachel left the office at lunch time telling herself almost savagely that she didn't care one way or the other. Tonight, there would be no outing with Toni. She would be thrown back on to her own resources and they had always been good enough before. She would throw herself into life in the city by herself, visit some of those chic shops, spend some of the money she had left, and spend more of her accumulating and generous salary.

Almost without knowing it, her steps led her to the little restaurant she had visited with Nick. She bought herself a white carnation from the little fat flower lady and ate in solitary splendour, lingering then on the way back to gaze into the little shops and to stand by the fountain and look with interest down the dark narrow streets that led off from the square, not wanting to go back to the office until the last possible minute.

An almost childish feeling of defiance seemed to suddenly overwhelm her, and with no thought for anything but to have her own way, even though Nick was not there to witness it, she broke the promise he had extracted from her and walked firmly from the square, heading into one of the darkest and most narrow streets.

It was darker than she had anticipated and half-way down, her own footsteps ringing in her ears, her courage almost failed her, only a dogged determination to defy Nick keeping her going. If he ever spoke to her again, she told herself angrily, she would tell him what she'd done, tell him, too, how ridiculous his advice had been.

Even so, she was rather relieved to step out into the sunshine of another square. It was very different here, though. The usual fountain was silent, clogged with leaves and papers; the place itself was dirty, houses crowding in on it with every shutter closed, almost as if the inhabitants had fled. There were no interesting shops here, no enticing restaurants; there was only poverty, dirt and a rather unlikely silence.

She walked a few yards into the area. It seemed that even the sunlight held a menace, her own shadow threatening, and as a chilling fear began to grow inside her she turned to retrace her steps, almost ready to run to get back to the security of her own little square, telling herself that it was all an overwrought imagination but suspecting that it was nothing of the kind.

She stopped even as she turned, momentarily transfixed with fear as she saw that she was no longer alone in the silent square, her ready temper refusing to come to her rescue as she found her way blocked by three young men who had come quietly and secretly into the square behind her.

One was tall, hefty, the other two a little weedy-looking, but there were three of them and they all had the same look in their eyes, a hungry, mean look like rats seeing a tasty meal.

'Predators, reared on the streets,' Nick's words came back to her with horrifying clarity and she found herself backing towards the silent fountain, looking frantically at the shuttered houses for help as the men slowly followed, saying nothing, moving line abreast, giving her no opportunity to dodge, however fast she might be on her feet.

'Hey, *signorina*!' There was a lilting menace in the voice that called to her; their smiles brought no humour to their faces. She felt the hard surround of the fountain dig into her back and realised that she had gone as far as she could go. There was now only flight and she knew that they would pursue, sure of their own territory, running her down perhaps in a place even more silent and lonely. Or they might have knives; almost certainly they would have. She was terrified to take her eyes from them in case they ran forward, and her predicament brought further soft laughter from them, laughter that raised the fine hairs on her arms and the back of her hands, paralysing her with fear.

Without warning, there was a voice from the end of the dark street that she had come down to the square, a voice that crackled with the force of an electrical storm, making her jump as much as the youths as they turned to face this unexpected attack from behind. The vicious flow of Italian that followed the sharp command had Rachel's eyes straining to see into the dark street, her heart leaping with surprise and joy as Nick stepped out into the sunlight.

Tall, dark clad and utterly menacing, he topped the tallest of her would-be assailants by at least two inches and, even though there were three of them, they glanced at each other uneasily because it was not his height that threatened; there was a violence in him that even Rachel in her relief saw. He wanted them to attack him, he wanted to kill them.

For a second they hesitated and he stepped forward, only one step, his arms by his sides, his face white with fury. It was too much for them. Their nerves were not up to this kind of cold violence. In a second, the square was empty except for Rachel and the man who stood tall and cold, watching her.

She stood against the fountain, glad of its support, her legs trembling and tears of fright and relief starting in her eyes as Nick remained exactly where he was, his silvery eyes glittering with anger.

Then she ran to him, her arms outstretched long before she got to him, rushing to safety, calling his name in a wild mixture of relief and panic.

'Nick! Nick!' She flung herself against him and for a second his arms enfolded her, gathering her against him, holding her tightly. Then he held her away, looking at her with cold, furious grey eyes before giving her the shaking of a lifetime.

Rachel was sobbing like a child as Nick took her arm and almost dragged her back through the dark, narrow street, out into the familiar sunlit square that she had so wilfully left, past the astonished eyes of lunch time strollers and out to his car parked by the edge of the road, almost appearing to have been abandoned in a hurry rather than parked.

He didn't exactly throw her into it but the thought was clearly in his mind and she sat huddled up as far away from him as possible, too shocked from her narrow escape, too scared of Nick to even notice his furious driving.

It was only as he brought the car to a juddering and slamming halt outside her flat and hauled her out that her sense of reality returned, making her fumble in her bag for her keys. A bag that was snatched from her hands as Nick found them himself and opened the door, propelling her through it and up the stairs to her own flat, removing her keys from her flat door and tossing them, with her bag, on to the floor as he slammed the door shut.

She bent with a little cry of fright to pick up the scattered contents but she was hauled to her feet, pulled against the powerful hardness of his chest.

'So!' he rasped violently, staring at her with wide-open, clear, cold eyes, speaking for the first time. 'Your promises, like everything else, are meaningless! You do as you wish, regardless of the consequences. You have even driven Toni into the defiance of courting you nightly in my absence!'

'How do you . . .' she began, trembling all over with shock, but she was not allowed to continue. She was not to be allowed even to speak.

'I know every move you make!' he roared. 'But today, by sheer chance, I saw you! I was late from the airport, another chance, and the sight of your fiery hair was unmistakable. You chose the only street to enter that is visible from the road. The fact that you stand here, safe and unmolested, is attributable solely to one unexpected circumstance after another. Do you realise how nearly fate left you to your own supposed ability to take care of yourself? Do you?' he shouted, shaking her again.

She could only stare at him, agreeing silently with every word that he roared at her, an overwhelming nausea beginning to grip her.

'You prefer the company of my cousin to mine. Very well,' he rasped. 'He is charming and friendly, safe and honourable. Do you even prefer the company of those hungry dogs to mine? If I had not appeared, what do you imagine would have been happening to you at this very moment? I think the contents of your purse were very much secondary to what they had in mind.'

Rachel pulled away from him, raced to the bathrom and slammed the door, leaning over the washbasin as the nausea overtook her, violently ill as her mind followed the harsh but true words that Nick had yelled at her.

After a while, she regained some composure, washed her hands and face, cleaned her teeth and walked unsteadily back to face Nick, realising what it would have meant to him if one of his staff had been attacked in broad daylight so close to his prestigious offices, especially an employee who had recently arrived from England.

He was just coming back into the flat having been, it seemed, to his car and he looked at her quickly as she came into the room.

'Later,' he said quietly as she made an attempt to speak. 'Sit down and drink this.' When she just stood staring at him, he put her into the nearest chair, pouring brandy from a little silver flask and holding it to her lips when her unsteady hands threatened to drop it. 'All of it,' he ordered quietly as she merely sipped a little. Then, as she finished the drink, he put it down and pulled her gently to her feet, looking at her searchingly for a moment and then lifting her into his arms, folding her against him comfortably like a hurt child. Walking into her bedroom, he placed her gently on her feet beside the bed, never speaking, never even looking at her, his eyes serious and his face grim as he dealt with the buttons of her dress, Rachel standing obediently, totally submissive as the dress slid to the floor and he pushed it aside. He bent to remove her shoes and then stood looking at her quietly.

'Sleep,' he ordered softly. 'Into bed, Rachel. The brandy will dull your nightmares and sleep will do the rest.'

When she didn't move but only stood with tear-filled brown eyes looking at some point midway between his chin and his waist, he leaned over and turned back the sheets, lifting her up and into bed, looking down for a second at her fragile shape in the delicate white slip before pulling the sheets over her and up to her chin.

'I've got to get back to work,' she whispered, her eyes tear-filled and enormous as he frowned down at her silently.

'I'll phone in for you,' he promised, walking away to the door of her bedroom. 'I very much doubt if they'll argue,' he added wryly. 'In spite of Stefanie, they'll probably assume that it is you who are welcoming me back home.'

She went to sleep crying, wishing that she *had* been welcoming him home, wishing that she had the right to. There had been no need for him to remind her of Stefanie; his future wife was on her mind all the time.

It was dark when she woke up and a glance at the clock told her that it was after eight. She slid from her bed and found her dressing-gown, tying it round her and

walking barefoot into the next room, surprised that the
lights were on. Nick was stretched on the settee reading
an English novel that she had brought with her.

'Oh! You came back!' Her heart leapt at the sight of
him but he watched her silently.

'Wrong. I never went,' he corrected, slowly sitting up
and getting to his feet. 'I thought you may need help at
some time but I can see that you're better now.'

'Did—did you have any lunch?' she found herself
asking, remembering that he had rescued her on his way
from the airport.

'No, I don't suppose that I did now that you mention
it.' He stretched stiffly and rubbed the back of his neck.
'Come to think of it, I'm starving.'

'I—I could make you a meal,' she volunteered in a
whisper. 'I've got things in the fridge.'

'You would consider eating with me, *signorina*?' he
said sarcastically and she turned her head away, colour
rushing into her unhappy face, determined not to
answer and argue with him.

'I'll ring round to the restaurant. There's a good little
place near here,' he said after a second's silence. 'They
will bring us a meal in a short time, more quickly than
you could get one ready and with less fuss to you.' She
didn't answer and he walked across to her, tilting her
chin, seeing the lingering distress.

'I'm sorry, Rachel,' he said softly. 'Sorry for your
terrifying experience, sorry for my violence in pointing
out to you the danger you were in and sorry for my nasty
remark just now.'

She looked up at him, her lips trembling, unable to say
anything for a second.

'It's all right,' she finally got out. 'You were right, of
course. I'm sorry, too, that you were in any danger there
and that you've felt it necessary to stay and—and watch
over me.'

'You watched over my father when he was—er—incapacitated,' he informed her with a little smile. 'Perhaps I have repaid the debt. And I was in no danger, except perhaps of committing murder.' Her trembling lips seemed to be fascinating him because he never looked away from them, finally giving in to the temptation and bending his head to allow his lips to simply drift over hers in a soft and healing little caress that held her spellbound. There was no demand, no fire, only a soothing stroking movement that eased her unhappiness.

'What would you like to eat?' he asked softly as he looked down at her, not touching her in any way.

'Not spaghetti,' she said with wide-eyed certainty, and his eyes were suddenly laughing like Toni's, his hand smoothing back her tousled bright hair in an unconscious gesture that was almost affectionate.

'Not spaghetti,' he conceded and turned to walk easily to the phone, looking back as she moved. 'Now where are you going?' he enquired softly, still with an air of a grown man who had a tender child to deal with.

'To get dressed.' She stopped when he shook his head in disagreement.

'Not really worth it. You need an early night. We will eat and then I will leave and let you get back to bed.'

He showed no surprise when she obeyed him and sat down on the settee, her hands in her lap, her bare feet demurely together like a small child.

'Would you like me to make some coffee?' he asked, coming back to her after phoning, apparently not about to delve any further into her defiant adventure.

'I'll make it.' She sprang up and he inclined his head in acceptance, sitting and taking up the book again as she left. He put it down with obvious reluctance as she returned and she was glad that the meal was delivered at that moment because it was clear that Nick had no desire to speak to her, and she could hardly blame him. She was thankful that the restaurant had been so astonishingly quick. Soon, Nick would go and she could be alone, trying to forget the cool indifference that was now in his eyes.

'We will eat here,' he ordered as the two waiters came in with heavy trays covered in white cloths. He indicated the table by the settee and they placed everything there, preparing to arrange the food, their eyes wandering to Rachel's dressing-gown-clad figure, no doubt drawing their own conclusions.

'Leave it!' Nick's sharp command had them looking guiltily at him and the money he held in his hand. 'You may collect the trays tomorrow,' he added with no room allowed for dissent. 'The lady who let you into the main hall will see to it.'

They left and Nick uncovered the food himself, arranging it on the table as Rachel watched irresolutely, not knowing where to sit, what to do.

'Come, eat,' he ordered. 'As I leave I will take the trays into the hall below so that you will not be troubled when they collect them.' He settled to eat, clearly very hungry, and after a little hesitation Rachel did likewise, sitting as far away as possible.

He had no intention of speaking, that much was clear, and his momentary burst of pity as she had come from the bedroom was now quite obviously over. There was nothing but silence, no contact whatever, and Rachel found it unbearable.

'Did you have a good trip?' she asked, needing to hear the sound of his voice with a longing that was a deep ache.

He nodded, not looking up. 'Successful.'

'Did—did you ring home from Japan, to Italy, I mean?' she heard herself asking, wanting to know if he had rung Stefanie Veccetti, wanting to hear him say no, unable to keep quiet.

He looked at her slowly and she could see that it was none of her business; his look told her that quite clearly.

'I normally do,' he remarked, staring at her intently. 'As Toni probably told you, I never let the reins drop,' he added curtly, still very obviously angered at her presumption in seeing his cousin.

'You—you work too hard . . .' she began falteringly but his harsh voice stopped her.

'When I need a nursemaid, I'll check your capabilities with my father and let you know,' he grated, going back to his meal.

'I didn't—I mean . . . Did you ring your father or anyone?' she stammered on, unable to stop.

He put his fork down and sat looking at her like a psychiatrist, obviously certain in his mind that she needed one, his clear grey eyes boring into hers, narrowing and then opening wide again.

'Yes, I rang my father and someone,' he said with care, his eyebrows raised mockingly. 'If you get your notebook, I'll try to give you a rough account of the conversations. It won't be perfect but you'll get the gist of it, enough to satisfy your mind as it is so obviously troubling you. I'm sure that my father will have no objections to your being in on the discussions we had, he being so fond of you. Probably Stefanie would not mind, either; she's reasonably easy-going. I think that you would probably like her as you are in no way jealous of her, your interest in me being merely on a business level. Maybe it would be a good idea to introduce you to her; she's very sweet more often than not.'

He picked up his fork and began to eat, glancing up at her from beneath dark brows as she blushed hotly, shame, humiliation and hurt flooding through her and jealousy striking like a hot knife.

'I'm sorry. I didn't mean to pry. It's none of my

business. I only . . .'

'Eat your dinner, Rachel,' he advised, not unkindly. 'After a good night's sleep you'll be back into your normal fighting stance, I'm sure, well able to continue with your impossible game.'

'It's not an impossible game!'' she cried hotly, her face so flushed that she felt fiery with the heat. 'I've told you that . . .'

'I'm well aware that you have told me many things,' he interrupted sardonically, 'painfully aware. I also know exactly how you feel.'

He said nothing else and she ate in silence, a silence that continued until he was ready to leave. There was nothing to say and she knew as she saw Nick's eyes wander several times to the book he had been reading that only politeness prevented him from picking it up and reading as he ate.

He took the trays into the hall downstairs and came back for his jacket, shrugging into it and then standing by the open door with cold, unreadable eyes on her.

'Lock the door,' he warned as she stood watching him nervously. She wanted to say something but there was really nothing to say. The vague hopes that she had that he would tell her that there was no truth in the rumour about himself and Princess Veccetti were all foolish, the foolish dreams of someone out of his world, as far away from someone like him as if she were an alien being.

Everyone at the main offices of Orsiani Italia knew about the forthcoming marriage, the man she had so reluctantly spoken to had made that quite clear, and Nick had now confirmed it, albeit obscurely. He was still standing there, looking at her.

'You can borrow the book if you like,' she suddenly burst out angrily, hurt that he had not even wanted to sit and talk to her. His eyes narrowed for a second as he continued to watch her closely.

'Thank you, but no. I rarely get the chance to read these days. Perhaps, though, when you get back to England you could send me a copy?' It was deliberately cruel, she felt, even though she realised that he had no idea of how she really felt for him, but he was accepting readily that there would come a time when they would never see each other again. The thought bit deeply and painfully into her.

'I will!' She raised her head proudly, her bright hair framing her pale face, and she moved to reach for the door, wanting him to go so that she could lock herself in with her misery.

He turned to leave and then, without warning, turned back.

'I phoned my father, the main office and Florence,' he informed her softly. 'I'll tell you all about it if you like, but details of what I said to Stefanie are not really available and that is the call that interests you, is it not?'

She looked away, wanting him to leave, horrified to find that there were tears in her eyes, embarrassed when he suddenly tilted her face with one strong brown hand.

'Tears?' he enquired intently, his eyes keen and grey on her face. 'Now why should that be with someone who wishes only to be an employee of mine? If I have a mistress in every city I know that it will be of no concern to you as you hate me so roundly, but in case you are concerned about my moral standing, I can assure you that I do not. I am far too busy. One is usually enough and, as you are unwilling to fill the role, I do not even have one at the moment. As to Stefanie, she was part of the normal pattern of my life long before I ever saw you and she will be very firmly established in her role in my life before too long.'

There was cruelty in every measured word and she tried to snatch her face away from the confining pressure of his hand, but he slid one powerful arm around her waist and drew her swiftly forward until she was looking up into his eyes, her own filled with tears that were a mixture now of pain and anger.

'The tears have cost you at least ten points in the game, I would think,' he said softly, his hand sliding from her face to cup her head beneath the bright fall of her hair. 'A disastrous loss of control, my little firebird.'

His dark head swooped down and she felt the warmth of his mouth covering hers in a deep, sensuous kiss that startled her in its unexpectedness and sweetness, a kiss that was over before she could gather her startled wits.

'Go to your lonely little bed, Rachel,' he advised, his eyes glittering with sudden amusement. 'What with one thing and another you have had a very bad day. I feel certain that most of the people in the office will know where I have spent the afternoon; most of them, too, will assume that your bed tonight will be far from cold and lonely. You will need to put on a good firm face in the morning. You need some sleep.'

He was gone before she could reply, even if she could have thought of anything to say. It mattered not to him what anyone thought and she mattered not to him either. He deserved all the hatred she could muster, but desolately she realised that she could not scrape together even one little bit, whatever he did.

CHAPTER SEVEN

RACHEL saw nothing of Nick during the rest of the week. Even though he resumed his normal daily routine, he semed rarely now to leave his own office, so that not even by accident did she catch so much as a glimpse of him.

In spite of her determination to amuse herself and enjoy her stay in Rome in her own way, she seemed to be too dispirited even to leave her flat most days. Certainly the effort to visit some of the places where she had been with Toni was too much for her, and apart from one evening when she went to visit Bill and Margaret for dinner, each night found her alone in her flat, Nick's face ever uppermost in her mind.

It was early Saturday evening when she received a frantic telephone call from Bill, the tone of his voice instantly alerting her to the fact that something really bad had happened.

'Rachel, can you come right now? Take a taxi and get here as fast as you can.' He seemed to be on the point of ringing off with no further explanation, clearly in some sort of a panic, and her years of working with him came straight to the surface.

'Tell me quickly what it is,' she said firmly, her steady voice obviously calming him a little because he explained briefly and quietly at once.

'Margaret fell on that damned marble step. She's definitely broken her arm and I'm getting her to hospital. Can you cope with the children?'

'I'll be right there.' It was Rachel who put down the phone, grabbing her bag and racing out to the street

after calling with great difficulty for a taxi, irritated
suddenly that she knew no Italian but managing
reasonably well with English and a sharp clear message
with her address.

Bill had somehow managed to create turmoil in the
intervening time. The children were in tears, Margaret
pale and in obvious pain and Bill shouting into the
telephone, his small grasp of the language deserting him
when he needed it most.

Finally, he got Margaret into the car and drove to the
hospital, leaving a wave of chaos behind him, including
two normally sensible little boys who now both wanted
to be comforted at once, a task Rachel managed quite
easily by sitting them on each side of her on the settee
and putting an arm round each small shoulder.

There was a meal to prepare, she told herself
methodically later when she had managed to calm them
and get them to help her to sort out the muddle that Bill
had left behind, and she suddenly felt the need to be in a
state of less than elegant apparel. Going up to the main
bedroom, she threw off her dress and donned an old pair
of Margaret's jeans and a faded shirt, bringing a smile at
last to the two worried little faces as the boys pointed out
that the jeans were too short on her tall, slender figure
and helped her to turn up the legs to mid-calf length.

After that, she was well in with them. She cleared up
the kitchen after she had made them a simple meal,
chatting to them as they ate, trying to keep them fully
occupied and off the subject of Mummy's asccident.
The bell rang soon after they had finished and it was
with two anxious pairs of hands clutching at her legs,
two worried little faces peering round from behind her,
that she opened the door to find Nick standing outside,
casually dressed in grey suede trousers and a white
lightweight sweater.

'Bill—Mr Taylor—is at the hospital,' she said breathlessly, the unexpected sight of him unnerving her completely.

'I know, I've just left him.' His eyes roamed over her borrowed garments and then fastened with interest on the two little boys clutching her tightly. 'I would like to come in,' he said softly, 'if you have no objections.'

'Sorry.' She moved aside and he stepped into the flat, his eyes on her flushed face and the protective arms that now secured the boys against her. 'How did you manage to be at the hospital?' she asked when he stood there looking at her and never offered any explanation.

'The language was beyond him at this stage in his learning,' he said quietly. 'He telephoned me at my flat and I went to sort out the affair. Apparently— Margaret?—has several allergies, and anaesthetics have to be chosen with care.'

'Ah, I didn't know that,' Rachel confessed in sudden understanding. 'That's why he was in a panic.'

'And being in a panic, naturally he called you,' he ended, with what may or not have been sarcasm. 'I can see that you have coped. He was a little anxious about the way everything had been landed on you without warning but apparently you are able to manage children as well as you manage everything else.'

He seemed to be about to leave and she suddenly didn't want him to, her mind frantically searching for something to keep him there.

'I'm just going to get the boys to bed then I'm going to make myself a meal,' she said, hurriedly searching for conversation. He stood watching her, still in an attitude of someone about to say goodnight and simply go. 'Is Margaret all right?'

'Yes. The break was bad but it is now set and they have decided to keep her in overnight. Bill,' he added suddenly, unexpectedly informal, 'is staying a while. He will eat at the hospital and tells you not to bother with anything for him.'

'Oh, yes.' She looked down and then, taking her courage firmly in hand, blurted out, 'Would you like to eat here? I have to get myself a meal; I can just as easily get two at once. I've fed the boys.'

For a moment she thought he was going to say coldly and finally, no, but he only hesitated for a second.

'If you are going to see to the children, then I will prepare a meal for both of us,' he said quietly, continuing when she opened her mouth to protest, 'You are busy, we are both probably hungry and it will be a relaxation for me. I am very good with omelettes,' he added proudly.

Rachel found herself nodding happily, her heart giving a little skip. At least she would see him for a little while longer. She hurried the boys up the small flight of stairs to the bathroom, trying not to be too conscious of the amused eyes on her jeans and shirt.

With the children safely bathed and into bed, she went down to help, but he turned from the cooker as she went in and in the time that she had been upstairs she could see that he had prepared a crisp salad and set the table for two. The promised omelette was about to be cooked.

'There is nothing to do,' he informed her. 'You can sit and wait for a minute and then we will eat. I will allow you to give an opinion about my culinary skills.'

'I—I think I'll just get back into my own clothes first,' Rachel said hurriedly as his eyes showed further signs of amusement at her apparel. 'I'll only be a minute.'

'An omelette will not wait,' he informed her sternly as she left, and she ran up the few steps feeling more happy than she had felt in days. He was treating her with a near normality. It meant nothing to him but to Rachel it was everything and she steadfastly refused to think of Stefanie Veccetti.

'Rachel!' The worried voice of Andrew called her into the boys' bedroom before she could even begin to change her clothes.

'Not asleep yet?' She stood in the doorway looking across at Bill's older son, who was propped up on one elbow waiting anxiously to have a word with her.

'No. I wanted to ask you, now that John is asleep, what do you really think? Will Mummy be all right?' he asked, with all the responsibility of an eight-year-old with a six-year-old brother to protect, and Rachel came in smiling to sit on the edge of the bed.

'Perfectly. She'll be home tomorrow and in a couple of weeks she'll be as good as new—better.'

'Have you ever had a broken arm, Rachel?' he enquired, wanting to know if she was speaking with any authority.

'Hundreds of them!' she exclaimed with a wild gesture that brought a quick grin of relief to his face, and he slid down in the bed laughing.

'Goodnight, Rachel.' His anxieties were lessened and he could sleep.

'Rachel! The omelette!' Nick's soft but firm call had her hurrying into the main bedroom, struggling out of the jeans and shirt and diving into the bathroom to quickly wash her hands and face, not wanting Nick to become impatient with her and spoil the little glow of happiness that was inside her.

'Rachel! This omelette is going to be . . .' Nick's voice from the open doorway of the bedroom brought her to a startled and embarrassed halt as she hurried back to dress.

His own voice had trailed away at the sight of her in

her white lacy bra and brief panties, her slender figure poised in mid-flight, her hair in gloriously colourful disarray around her shoulders, and for a second they simply stared at each other while Rachel's face flushed in painful confusion.

'The omelette is going cold,' he said in a quiet voice suddenly husky and slow, never moving from the door, his eyes seemingly unable to stop their vibrant appraisal of her.

'I—I'm sorry. I'll come now. Andrew wanted ...'

She reached for her dress, her eyes never leaving him, and held it in front of her, her face filled with an embarrassed shyness that suddenly seemed to annoy him.

'I'm serving dinner now,' he said, turning away and going back down the steps.

She bit her lip in anxiety. He had held her on the beach with less clothes than she had been wearing just then, but somehow it was different. This was more intimate and she was sure that he was annoyed that she had placed him in this awkward position by her failure to answer when he had called upstairs.

She was still flushed and confused when she went down to the kitchen where he had served the food.

'Eat it while it's hot and tell me if you like it,' he said briefly without looking at her, seating himself opposite and beginning to eat. He was clearly going to ignore the incident, but she couldn't. It was sitting too huge and painful in her mind, causing a silence that would grow as the meal progressed.

'I'm sorry about—about ... Andrew wanted to ask me if ...'

Nick looked up at her then, his eyes meeting hers and then roaming over her flushed cheeks.

'Does it matter so much?' he enquired quietly. 'I've

seen you when you were wearing less and imagined you in even less than that. I imagine too that I am not the only man to have seen you like that, you having been so recently engaged,' he added with a quick and unexpected aggression.

It ended any hopes that she may have had that the meal would be a peaceful and healing time between them. It hurt her, too, very badly. Chris had never seen her like that. She had never allowed any kind of intimacy, had never surrendered with Chris as she had already done twice in Nick's arms. She had never even realised that there was a fire inside her until Nick had kissed her and held her.

She didn't reply, it seemed to be of little point, and the golden omelette became cotton wool and paper in her mouth as she followed his lead and bent her head to her meal.

Bill came back at nine, and not a moment too soon for Rachel. She had finished her meal with no further attempt at conversation and Nick had not asked what she thought of his efforts. Together, with no further discussion, they had cleared away and washed the dishes, not speaking at all, as if they had been arguing violently. It was with a feeling of numb indifference that Rachel accepted Nick's offer to drive her back to her flat and the only words that were spoken between them were Rachel's when she said, 'Thank you. Goodnight,' as she got out of his car. He didn't even reply to that, his brief nod being the only move he was prepared to make.

He had driven off before she had even walked up the shallow steps to the front door and, knowing that he had, her heart leapt with fright when, as she stood fitting her key in the lock, a hand came to her shoulder and a voice spoke her name.

'Rachel.'

She spun round in a quick burst of shock at the sound
of the voice, her eyes widening in disbelief.

'Chris!' For a second she couldn't believe that it was
actually Chris standing there, certain that she must be
hallucinating, but he was very real and the arms that
hugged her to him were urgent and very much the arms
she had known for so long.

'I'm parked round the corner,' he said in a minute,
holding her away and looking down into her startled
face. 'The woman in the bottom flat told me you were
out so I just waited. I had to see you.'

'I was at Bill Taylor's. Margaret broke her arm. I've
been looking after the boys,' she explained, staring at
him in astonishment. 'Chris! What are you doing here?
Why aren't you in Zarein?'

'Can we go inside, do you think?' he asked quietly. 'I
want to talk to you, to have a good look at you. It's dark
here and I can hardly see you.'

'Yes. Yes, of course.' She was still feeling stunned at
the unexpected sight of him, too surprised to feel
anything but her original astonishment, and he followed
her up the stairs to her flat, walking in and looking
round in surprised approval as she switched on the
lamps.

'Very nice! You have come up in the world, Rachel,
love,' he commented, his eyes on the elegance of her
sitting-room, the old high ceilings, the tasteful and
expensive furniture, every colour blending with satisfy-
ing harmony. 'I bet this costs you a small fortune.'

'It doesn't cost anything,' Rachel began to explain,
but stopped any discussion of the advangtages of her
new job to turn to him for explanations of his own.
'Chris, what are you doing in Rome? I thought you only
got leave once every six months? It's only a matter of
weeks since you went out there.'

He suddenly sat down, avoiding her eyes for a second and then looking up at her ruefully, a small boy come to confess his sins in the certain knowledge that they would be forgiven.

'I wanted to see you,' he said in a quiet and oddly forlorn voice. 'I found out that things aren't the same when you're not there. I can stick it out with no difficulty, so don't go saying that I haven't even got started before I'm quitting, Rachel,' he added hurriedly when he saw the look on her face and totally misunderstood it. 'It's just that I need to know that you're there, waiting for me.'

She just stood there looking down at him, her mind racing wildly, unable to believe just what she was hearing. Things weren't the same when she was not around; he needed to know that she was there waiting. Good old Rachel. Tell me what to do, Rachel. Forget that I went off and left for two years without any thought but my own glory and benefit. How right she had been, she thought with a great easing of her mind. She had been nothing but a prop to Chris, a constant factor in his life.

A few of the bitter words that Nick had said to her when she had accused him so violently of separating her from Chris came back into her mind, and now she could only silently agree with him. She could also see with great clarity the difference between the two men. Nick needed no props. Nick's wife would be safe, protected, with no need to hold up Nick's flagging ego. It was like comparing a man and a boy.

'I really don't know what you expect me to do about all this, Chris,' she remarked quietly, unwilling even now to see him hurt, even though he had hurt her. 'You're there for two years and then anything might happen. You might get a contract anywhere in the world. You told me that.'

'I know. It's true. But it needn't make any difference, Rachel. If it was a decent place you could be there, and you wouldn't need a job. If the contract was in a place like Zarein, then you could stay in England; we could have a nice house and everything you needed. It would work out fine.'

'For you,' Rachel said quietly. 'I rather think we are treading the same old ground again, aren't we?'

'No!' he insisted, his face a little red at her pointed statement. 'Before, I didn't object to the wedding being cancelled because I thought it would be better, better for you,' he added quickly. 'But it's not better. I just don't want to think that you're out of my life, Rachel.'

'I am out of your life, Chris,' Rachel told him quietly, but with a finality that had him looking at her intently. 'I cannot and will not spend the rest of my life being a backdrop to your future.'

'I'm asking you to marry me! I want you to marry me now, in Rome!' he cried, springing up and taking her by the shoulders. 'I don't want to go back there without being married to you.'

'Chris, I won't marry you. Not now in Rome and not anywhere ever,' she said with a quiet determination that had him staring at her in disbelief. 'I just do not want to marry you. The Zarein job was really a blessing; marriage would have been a terrible mistake for both of us.'

'You don't mean it! You can't! I know you were angry and hurt, but we'll get over it. You've been angry with me plenty of times before and we've always made it up.'

'Look, understand, Chris, that I just don't want to marry you! The sooner you accept that fact, the sooner I can offer you a drink and we can talk like old friends.'

'I'm not an old friend, for God's sake!' he suddenly

yelled. 'I'm in love with you! You're my girl!'

'But I am not in love with you, Chris, and I am not any longer your girl,' Rachel said with an air about her that made him stop and stare at her.

An unexpected noise from the doorway had them both turning at once and Rachel's heart almost stopped in shock as she saw Nick standing just inside the room leaning against the frame of the partly open door, tossing a small bunch of keys in his hand, an air about him that stated clearly that he was more than used to making this type of unannounced entry.

'I'm sorry, *cara*. I startled you,' he said softly, the endearment sliding from his lips with what seemed to be the ease of familiarity, his eyes caressing and openly possessive as he looked at her. 'I imagined that you would have heard my keys in the lock, but I see that you have an old friend here.'

Rachel's face slowly flushed at the picture he had so subtly painted, and Chris looked slowly from Nick to her guilty face and back to the keys in Nick's hand. He might be selfish, but he was not stupid, and anyone would have had to be blind to miss the implications of that moment.

'Oh!' The slow word of understanding left Chris's lips and fell into a silence that was painful to Rachel and clearly delightful to Nick. 'I'm sorry, Rachel. I didn't know. I had no idea that you and—that.' He looked at her as if he could not in any way believe the evidence of his own eyes but obviously the evidence was too overwhelming to disbelieve. Worse than anything, she just couldn't seem to say a word; her eyes were locked with the smiling, caressing gaze of Nick's glittering, grey eyes. 'Never mind the drink, Rachel. I'll be going, I think.'

Chris moved to the door, his face flushed, too, with embarrassment at the feelings that seemed to be swirling round Nick and Rachel, because Nick's eyes were shutting out everything and everyone except the woman he watched.

'You have leave?' Nick suddenly said as Chris approached the door. 'The time has flown more quickly than I realised.'

In a flash, he was no longer the lover of the girl Chris had left to seek a new life for himself; he was Orsiani, in control and demanding an explanation. Even Rachel was sufficiently aware to realise this swift and alarming change.

'I did a swop for a few days,' Chris said with the almost defiant air that Rachel knew so well, an attitude he adopted when he had been thwarted in some scheme. 'I wanted to see Rachel but I may as well get back to the job. It's cool in Italy after Zarein,' he suddenly added with a small, spiteful look at Rachel's still stunned face.

'I can see that it would be,' Nick observed, stepping aside. 'I hope your little excursion will not delay your first report to me?'

'End of the month, Mr Orsiani,' Chris said with a little more grace, seeming to realise that he still had his job in spite of taking leave without permission and trying to persuade Rachel to marry him when she was so clearly the property of the boss. 'Cheerio, Rachel,' he added, not looking in her direction.

Her instinct to protect him sprang to the surface at once.

'Chris!' She moved forward but he never even looked round; he was already through the door and Nick shut it firmly, standing with his back to it and showing no sign of being movable.

'I want to see Chris out!' she said sharply, raging inside at Nick's beastly trick, temper at last drowning her embarrassment. 'I want to talk to him.'

'He is quite capable of finding the front door,' Nick informed her steadily, 'and you have already spoken to him. I heard the most interesting parts of the conversation and as far as I can see there is nothing more to be said. You will certainly not be seeing him again.'

The front door slammed and Rachel could imagine Chris's face now. It would be filled with an almost adolescent rage and he would have placed all the blame squarely on her shoulders before he had driven many yards. There was little point now in trying to push Nick aside; not that she would have had much success anyway, she told herself furiously.

'How did you get in here?' she demanded angrily, free now to turn her attention to him.

'My keys,' he said with surprise and the air of someone who was being attacked for no reason whatever. He dangled them under her nose and then put them into his pocket.

'You can just give me those!' she stormed, glaring at him, and his eyes gleamed with interest, his smile teasing and irritating.

'You can always try to get them,' he suggested softly, laughter in his voice.

'Stop hedging around the point!' Rachel cried, her face flushing again with new embarrassment. 'You know what Chris thinks now, don't you? You deliberately allowed him to get the impression that you—that you . . .'

'That I am your lover and that I keep you here in our little nest of love,' he finished for her. 'You think that he got the message?' he asked, his eyes holding hers as she suddenly found herself short of breath. 'I would be pleased to have your opinion as an onlooker. He seemed to have seen the light, but one never knows.'

'Why did you come back? Where did you get those

keys from? And how dare you do this?' Rachel stormed,
getting her second wind.

'You would like your answers one at a time, briefly, or
in one continuous narrative?' he queried with infuriat-
ing reasonableness. 'It is almost ten-thirty,' he added,
glancing at his watch. 'Perhaps it would be better if I
made the whole thing into a bedtime story?' When she
didn't answer but merely continued to glare up at him,
he leaned back against the door and crossed his legs
elegantly, his arms folded across his chest.

'This house and the flats it contains came on to the
market about a year ago. I bought it,' he explained. 'We
like to have property to house our managers and this was
suitable. The lady in the lower flat was already here; she
is an inquisitive little person who takes on the job of
concierge more to pass her time and satisfy her curiosity
than for any monetary gain. She followed me around
happily when I came to view the house and this was the
only flat vacant. I found it charming and decided to have
it furnished and decorated as you now see it. She
enquired if I would like her to find a tenant for me. I told
her that I would keep it for my mistress and she found
the idea amusing.'

He looked into Rachel's slowly boiling face, an
amusement in his own eyes that infuriated her.
'Naturally, when you moved in, she realised that I had
discovered the mistress that I wanted and she was quite
satisfied. I have keys because the flat is mine. I came back
because she rang to tell me that a man had been hanging
around and that he had come up here with you. She was
quite frantic and, knowing your record for impetuosity,
I felt the need to investigate.'

He stopped at that, clearly thinking that this little tale

would do, but it would not do for Rachel.

'In the first place,' she began heatedly. 'You have no
business whatever to have keys to my flat, even if the
company owns it. I pay the rent and nobody else has any
right to have keys! And in the second place, you can just
get down there and tell your friendly little busybody that
I am merely an employee of Orsiani Italia!'

'You pay the rent, *signorina*?' he enquired mockingly.
'To whom do you pay it? You are being robbed, I fear,
and it must obviously be investigated.'

'It—it's stopped from my salary just like everybody
else's,' Rachel said, a little of the certainty leaving her
eyes as he smiled mockingly down at her. 'When I came
here I asked that—that woman downstairs, because
I thought she was the landlady, but she said ... she
said ...'

'What did she say that is so very frightening to
reveal?' Nick asked softly. 'May I suggest that she said
that I took care of the rent? As to it being stopped from
your salary, yes, everyone else has their rent stopped at
source. There is a very generous allowance here for the
English party and, while I will admit to being generous,
I am not Father Christmas, except to you. When the
computer in the wages section comes to your name, it
makes a spritely little leap over the deductions for rent of
your flat; a discreet curtain is drawn over the whole
thing. Of course, they know your address and also they
know that I own the house. They therefore naturally
know that you are my mistress. I may not possess you
but I most certainly keep you, Rachel.'

She flew at him, both hands raised, goaded beyond
words, her temper out of control.

'You foul beast! You nasty, loathsome, hideous ...'

He caught her wrists and held them at her sides as she
struggled wildly, his eyes gleaming in amusement as her

fiery hair fell around her face and her dark eyes glared at him with hatred, and then he pulled her arms behind her, grasping both wrists in one powerful hand, leaving her raging and helpless as he drew her nearer.

'You have used your former fiancé as an excuse to escape me in the past, but now that will not do at all,' he said with a quiet triumph. 'You do not love him and you will not marry him. I heard all that myself. What excuse will you use this time, my little fireball?'

'I don't need any excuse!' she yelled at him, her eyes blazing with fury. 'I hate you!'

'Do you?' he asked quietly, letting her go and just standing looking down at her. 'How much?'

'More than you'll ever know,' she informed him nastily, a little subdued at his sudden quiet. 'It's a pity that I didn't know you'd be sneaking in. If I had, I could have arranged a nice love scene to greet you; Chris was more than willing!'

Her goading did not, as she had expected, bring a return to his usual anger. Instead, he just looked at her steadily, but his eyes were no longer mocking, they were like silver ice.

'If I had found what I half expected to find,' he said with deadly quiet, 'your friend would not now be on the way back to a post he has deserted to follow a selfish whim. He would still be here, unable, I think, to follow any sort of occupation for quite a few months. Nobody will touch you! It is only my knowledge of Toni's character that has kept him safe, and his early and sensible withdrawal from the scene proves his wisdom. If anyone ever lays a hand on you they will not forget it for the rest of their lives!'

She stared at him for a second, her face white, a chill of fear running down her spine as it had done the first time she saw him.

'You—you make me feel like—like the property of a gangster,' she whispered.

'Feel whatever you like,' he advised her harshly. 'I want you and I will not allow competition. Nobody will get the chance to snatch you from my grasp because I would follow you and bring you back!'

'How can you talk like that?' she cried, looking at him in astonishment. 'You know the facts as far as we are concerned. Do you imagine that I can ignore the woman in your life? You're behaving as if Stefanie Veccetti doesn't exist!'

'She has nothing to do with the way we feel!' he parried impatiently. 'You and I are part of the same fire and if I saw you across the heads of a crowd, I would come for you. What is between us is inevitable, written in the stars and undeniable, Look at me and deny it, Rachel!'

CHAPTER EIGHT

RACHEL turned her back on him, still shivering from the burst of anger and the chilling fear that had raced along her spine, rubbing her wrists where his strong fingers had grasped her and held her fast.

'Sometimes—sometimes,' she whispered shakily. 'I could really kill you. You make me so angry.'

'I know.' He moved behind her, pulling her against him, his arm tightly round her waist, his face buried in her hair. 'That is how we feel about each other—violent. Whatever separated us, we would move towards each other with an unerring instinct because we can neither of us help it. From the moment that we met, it has been there, this desire.'

His free hand moved inside the neck of her dress, not hesitantly or seductively but with a rough urgency, plunging downwards to push aside her lacy bra and close with an almost savage pleasure over her breast, his voice murmuring in his own language against her hair as he held her tightly against him.

'Nick! Don't!' She was unable to move, unable in any way to avoid his searching fingers, and her plaintive gasp was ignored as he simply continued as if she had never spoken, his hand possessive on her breast, his pleasure whispered into the shining clouds of her hair.

'It is how we will make love,' he said thickly, 'with a feverish desire to almost destroy each other. It has always been there, a compulsive urge to possess each other. We are like passionate enemies. It is almost a death

136

wish and I can think of nothing else because it has begun to rule my life.'

She turned her face to look at him, almost afraid to see his face after the deep vibrancy in his voice, and he moved his hands to her shoudlers, spinning her roughly towards him, his mouth claiming hers savagely as he held her so tightly that breathing was almost impossible.

'You're hurting me, Nick!' She managed to pull her head away, his passion frightening her, and he slackened his grip a little, his mouth hot on her cheeks.

'You frustrate me in every way, turn me into someone with no hold on reality, no control over my own destiny,' he whispered huskily. 'I see only you. I think of nothing else.'

His hand moved against her back, sliding down the zip of her dress, his lips coaxing hers when she murmured a little word of alarm.

'We are only going back to where we have been before,' he murmured against her lips as her dress slid to the floor under the pressure of his urging hands. 'Tonight when you stood so startled in that bedroom and I wanted to close the door and devour you.'

'You were angry with me,' Rachel reminded him in a soft, trembling voice, her body beginning to flare with heat and move restlessly against him, her head thrown back as his lips moved over the velvet skin of her throat.

'I am always angry with you, you little wild cat,' he breathed, pushing aside the straps of her bra, his teeth nibbling at her shoulder almost to the point of pain. 'I don't want any woman to make me feel like this, to obsess me day and night, to make me know that if she flees I must follow, however long it takes.'

There was an almost angry acceptance of her power over him in his voice, an intensity in his body as if he was listening with every part of him to the restless movements of her own. Tentatively, almost as an experiment, she ran her hand along the side of his face, moved her lips to the strong jawline and trailed delicate kisses along its length, feeling him stiffen, his fingers tightening on her as his breathing deepened.

'Touch me,' he whispered thickly. 'Confess to wanting me as I want you. Let the fire burn you, Rachel.'

And she was suddenly fiercely glad of the power she had over him, a power he had confessed to feeling. She felt the same, as if every path she took must lead to Nick, as if she was trapped in a maze where every turning led to him. She reached out, no longer a victim but a willing and eager participant, her hands sliding beneath the luxury of his sweater, following her instincts to move with caressing palms against his smooth back, her heart leaping at his sharp intake of breath.

'Don't stop touching me,' he groaned. 'Never stop, Rachel. I seem to have waited a whole lifetime!'

It was as if her touch had released all the fire in both of them and their lips clung together frantically, their bodies strained towards each other in a fierce and passionate explosion that it seemed could never end. Her hands pulled with urgent desperation at his sweater until he tore it over his head and flung it to the carpet, their mouths claiming each other immediately, refusing to be parted.

Nick's hands moved over her with an intimate certainty as her bra followed his sweater to the carpet, his hands returning to her skin with urgent caresses until she felt drugged with pleasure, falling into a timeless world that held only the two of them.

'How long do you think I can go on without taking you?' he demanded, his lips leaving hers to gasp for air, his hands tight on her slender hips. His eyes were dark

and burning, not silver any more, as he looked down at
her. His face was tight and harsh, his pupils enlarged to
deep black pools.

She wound her arms more tightly around him,
moaning softly as her tongue made erratic patterns in
the crisp black hairs on his brown chest, and he grasped
her hair, forcing her head back.

'You're torturing me,' he gasped, making her meet
his eyes again, his breath leaving him in a harsh
shuddering sigh at what he saw on her face.

'*Dio!* You turn me into a savage!' he rasped, sweeping
her up into his arms and striding to the bedroom as she
wound her arms around his neck and covered his face
with wild, hot kisses.

He shouldered the door open, sparing no time to close
it, laying her on the bed and looking down at her for a
second, his breathing harsh and uneven before he came
down to join her. He pulled her fiercely to him, his hand
sliding the length of her slender leg, his mouth hot on
her breast as she twisted wildly in his arms, consumed by
her own fire, her own love for him.

'Rachel!' he groaned. 'Like a wild flame. Like an
uncontrolled fire!' His lips devoured her and she clung
to him with the same ferocity, determined to keep him,
knowing that without him life might as well end. By
some magical means, by some strange power outside all
understanding, she had found the one man, the only
man, who could put this life and fire into her, and she
loved him with a desperation that cut all other things
from her mind.

He raised his head to look at her as his hand moved to
finally unveil her, to take away the last item that covered
the slender fiery statue, and she closed her eyes in
acceptance, knowing that she would belong to him for as
long as she lived.

But suddenly his hand stilled, the fire seemed to leave his fingertips and she felt cold, alone, knowing without opening her eyes that he had withdrawn from her, no longer wanting her.

She opened her eyes and he was leaning over her, watching her face, a look in his eyes that she failed to understand, a look almost of shock. He rolled away from her and stood beside the bed, his back towards her, his head thrown back as he took in great gasps of air like a dying man.

'Nick!' Her little plea of anguish had him lowering his head and the words she heard were Italian, meaningless to her, but she knew that something, undoubtedly her, had drained him of all passion with a suddenness that seemed impossible. It was probably her eagerness to belong to him, probably her lack of experience that had finally reached him and left him taut and distant, or maybe he had realised that, beside Princess Veccetti, she was not worth the risk of an involvement.

She rolled over on to her stomach, trembling with need, feeling ashamed and inadequate, her deep harsh sobs stifled in the pillow.

'Rachel!' He was beside her instantly, lifting her even when she struggled to be free, pulling her into his arms and cradling her there.

'What—what did I do?' she sobbed, tears raining down her face.

'Nothing,' he soothed quietly, kissing her tears with an unknown tenderness as if she was a child. He put her securely in her dressing-gown and then held her close again, rocking her in his arms. 'You did nothing, Rachel,' he repeated softly. 'It is I. Suddenly, I saw you. I saw you I think for the first time. I know that I have left you hurting but I cannot make love to you.'

She started at him uncomprehendingly as he bent to kiss her again.

'I must go,' he said quietly. 'I'm leaving you unhappy and hurting, alone and lost, but I must go. There is too much heat between us for it to be possible for me to stay. I doubt my ability to comfort you and stay in any way responsible for my actions.' He looked at her for a second and then placed a light kiss on her trembling lips.

'Forgive me, *cara*,' he begged softly, almost as if he meant it, and then he was gone and she heard the flat door close a few minutes later.

'Suddenly I saw you. I saw you for the first time.' And saw that she was not Stefanie Veccetti, saw that she was only herself, Rachel Gordon, a minor cog in a mighty firm, a possible liability. She flung herself back on the pillows and wept.

For a man who was never out of his office, it suddenly seemed that he was never in it, and Rachel had no doubts as to why. He didn't want to see her and he was fast approaching his wedding day. She moved through the building like a slender, pale ghost, her bright hair emphasising the pallor of her face.

Margaret came home and Rachel dined with them several times, feeling it to be almost an obligation because she had no interest or joy in anything any more. To eat was an imposition and she steadily lost weight, lost it with alarming rapidity until she felt only lightly attached to the earth.

She saw no one that she knew apart from the Taylors. Toni, true to his word, had kept away and her constant dread was the fast-approaching reception that she would be expected to attend. Orsiani Italia were launching a new helicopter and all of the staff were invited guests at the launching.

A huge buffet dinner was to be held in an enormous house on a great country estate not far from Rome. The press were invited and nothing must go wrong. Some of the staff had visited the great house before, and excitement was high as the day approached.

There was no escaping. Nick would be there and she knew that this would be a suitable occasion for his forthcoming marriage to be leaked to the press, or even to be formally announced. She felt that it would be her death sentence and that she would be forced to witness the end of her own life, but she was trapped into the silent power that had been her relationship with Nick and there was no one to turn to, no one to help her out of her distressing trap.

On the day of the reception Bill and Margaret picked her up to drive her out there, both bubbling with anticipation, and Rachel had to make an enormous effort to appear to be in any way normal.

The place was impressive, a huge country house that was almost like a palace and had probably been just that, according to Bill. The wide, surrounding lawns left it standing white and proud like a gem on green velvet, the perfect place for a wealthy industrialist to announce his engagement to a princess, and Rachel felt that it would surely be here, tonight, that the announcement would be made.

It was early evening, still light though the day was fast fading, and when they arrived the affair seemed to be in full swing. Even so, no one was as yet eating and, though a small orchestra played in one of the main rooms, a room big enough to have been a ballroom, very few couples were dancing.

There was an air of expectancy and Rachel was not quite sure why. She saw no sign of Nick's future wife although she looked steadfastly around to find her, feeling that this torture was a necessity, but Toni was there and he came across to her as soon as he saw her.

'You look very beautiful, Rachel,' he said softly, admiring the pale turquoise dress she wore, 'though I think perhaps that you do not look too happy.'

'I'm quite all right.' She smiled, taking the arm he offered. 'What are they all waiting for, the helicopter?'

'Naturally. It should be here soon and then the festivities can begin. We usually do this sort of thing,' he laughed. 'It is a good excuse to celebrate.'

He began to lead her out to the terrace as other couples also drifted out that way, everyone in fact moving in the same direction.

'It's time,' Toni said with satisfaction. 'It should be here soon.'

'Who—who will bring it?' Rachel asked, really knowing the answer already and dreading the moment when Toni would confirm it.

'Nick, of course! When we need a show, we call in the expert.' He grinned. 'But tonight I think he will behave himself, so do not look so worried.'

She couldn't help it. Thoughts, fears, dreads all chased themselves around in her head. Suppose he ignored her? Suppose Stefanie Veccetti arrived with him? Suppose he should decide to bring it in with the same frightening skill he had shown before? She wouldn't be able to watch.

She found herself in a little group come together for the single purpose of watching for Nick. His father had seen her and came across to speak. Bill and Margaret had wandered across to join her, too, and all were anxiously scanning the sky, a sky that was now streaked with colour, midnight blue with the red flare of the dying sun low on the horizon.

'There he is!' Some sharp-eyed girl in the crowd saw

him first and then one after another they saw him, a tiny speck of dark against the dying sun, more clearly visible seconds later against the midnight blue as the sun's rays caught the silver metal of the helicopter and its lights were bright against the darker background.

'He's high,' Toni remarked softly to his uncle as they both watched.

'Too damned high,' Vincenzo Orsiani muttered. 'He promised faithfully, no tricks.' His tone made Rachel's heart sink as she watched the helicopter's lights, the glitter of its silver skin as it came nearer.

Soon, he was directly overhead and every face on the terrace was turned upwards to watch, but he seemed to be making no move to land.

'Damn you, Nick, get it down here!' his father growled softly and then, as if in answer, the helicopter began to fall, spiralling strangely, appearing to change direction and circle, only to spiral again in a high and distant dance. It seemed to be almost like the erratic flight of a dragonfly and there was applause from the packed terrace, but Rachel hardly heard the excited comments.

'Look at Nick!'

'He can practically make these machines sing!'

'That's one I've never seen before!'

Her eyes were drawn to Toni and to Nick's father and there was no admiration on their faces, only an increasing anxiety, an anxiety that Vincenzo Orsiani had not shown when his son had fallen like a diving bird to the villa by the sea. But it was Bill who put their fears into words, his head tilted, listening to the engine, the authority of years of knowledge in his voice.

'My God! He's in trouble,' he muttered quietly and Rachel's heart seemed to stop beating.

The erratic and spectacular descent continued,

delighting the crowd but leaving the little group who stood apart silent and pale. There was a gasp as the engine suddenly stopped. Within a second it started again, a hoarse, harsh note that quickly changed to smooth power, but in that second he seemed to be falling out of the sky and Rachel's cry had Toni's arm tightly around her.

'Nick! Oh, Nick!' She stared at the sky, willing him to live, willing him to safety, trembling violently when it happened twice more, his recovery spectacular each time.

'He's terrific! I'd no idea you could do that with a helicopter.'

The enthusiastic voice from the crowd was clearly heard above the now steady roar of the machine and Bill muttered under his breath, 'You can't, but by God, he's doing it!'

They watched, a strange assortment of people: the ignorant, excited; the knowledgeable, terrified; and when at last, after what seemed to Rachel to be the whole of a lifetime, he brought the machine down on the far edge of the wide lawn, there was uproar. People raced across to congratulate him as he climbed out, his usual white helmet tossed on to the seat, his tall, powerful figure in black sweater and jeans.

'Fabulous!'They crowded around him enthusiastically as if he was a visiting pop star. 'That was some stunt, Nick!'

'I can only agree,' he remarked with a smile as he came up the steps to join the group there who had not moved to greet him, his only comment to his father and Toni a raised eyebrow and a quizzical grin. 'Some stunt,' he repeated quietly, patting his father affectionately on the back.

And then his eyes sought Rachel's. She was still in the

tight circle of Toni's arm, her face completely white, her dark eyes enormous as for a second they looked at each other, and then she broke free and ran, racing into the house and upstairs to the nearest bathroom to lock herself in and weep hysterically.

She had no idea how long she was there, her mind suddenly refusing to function at all except to see the deep blue of the sky, the awesome height, the spiralling, falling machine and to remember her prayers as Nick seemed to be falling to certain death.

After a while, she dried her eyes and made an attempt to remove the signs of her grief, with only limited success. She couldn't stay there all evening, although she would gladly have done so. She realised that she had made a fool of herself by racing off like that and she realised, too, that she had no right to show this tearing grief for Nick. Toni was a friend, he understood, but to Nick's father she was just a girl he had taken to, a girl who shared with him a little amusement, a little adventure he had found in a foreign land. He would be shocked at her manner of behaving when his son was so soon to be married, and Nick would be embarrassed, probably annoyed, because she had no idea how many people had seen her flight. It would be better if she could just simply fade away into the night and go back to her flat.

She had to face it, though, and she picked up her evening bag and opened the door. Nick was there. He was leaning against the opposite wall, his eyes on the door as if he had been patiently waiting for ages—she knew the limits of Nick's patience. He would be here to tell her about her conduct, to demand an explanation. Her eyes met his with no excuses in them.

He straightened up and let his gaze wander over her face, seeing her distress, the remains of her tears and her trembling lips. Then he stepped forward, simply holding out his hand to her, his eyes never leaving hers as she came forward to meet him, to find her hand taken in both of his and raised gently to his lips, before he led her downstairs, his strong fingers entwined with hers.

'Shouldn't you be making a speech or something, or—or talking to your father?' she whispered as they reached the room where couples were now dancing, but he shook his head and pulled her gently into his arms, moving into the rhythm of the dance, holding her close.

'I've spoken to him already and he will make any necessary speeches,' he said softly, merely nodding pleasantly to the people who wanted to speak to him, moving to the music, his arms steadily pulling her closer until she was tightly in his arms, his face against her hair.

'I—I'm sorry that I ran off like that and—and everybody saw it and . . .' she began in a choked voice but he silenced her by lifting the hand he held and kissing her palm softly.

It was so unlike Nick, this gentleness, and she felt tears beginning again merely because he was tender, a foolish reaction to behaviour she had not expected.

'Do you want to eat?' he asked after a while, pulling back to look at her, but she looked up at him and shook her head, in no way in control of her emotions.

'No. I can't—I . . .' Tears came back into her eyes and he pulled her tightly against him, his hand moving to massage the nape of her neck, soothing and gentle.

'It's all over,' he murmured against her hair. 'My feet are firmly on the ground. It's finished. Try to forget it. Talk to me.'

'I can't. Oh, Nick!'

He stopped dancing, lifting her face, looking deeply into her eyes, and she didn't even try to hide what was there for him to see.

His long fingers stroked her face, moved softly across her lips, and his eyes darkened as she kissed his fingertips, unable to help it.

'Let's go,' he said quietly, his arm tightly around her waist as they walked from the room. He ignored all the eyes that were turned to them as if there was nobody else there.

He stopped briefly by Toni, his fist pushing Toni's chin in an affectionate gesture.

'Thanks, cousin,' he said gently.

'Is she all right?' Toni asked, his eyes on Rachel, and Nick looked down at her as their eyes met.

'She will be,' he said quietly, drawing her closer. 'Don't move that machine by one inch,' he warned and Toni laughed, his eyebrows raised.

'Do I look insane?' he returned as they walked out into the warm night.

Outside, Nick's arm fell away and he took her hand again, neither of them speaking, too filled with emotion to trust any words. He started his car and drove down the long drive to join the road to Rome.

'Toni brought my car,' he volunteered into the vibrant silence between them, seeming to wish to mention some mundane thing to take the emotional charge from the atmosphere. 'My father will take him back to the city.'

'Nick,' she half whispered. 'Should we have stayed? I would have been all right. People will think ...'

'People will be right,' he said softly. 'I did not want to stay. I wanted to be with you, alone. Do you care any more what people think, Rachel?'

'No,' she sighed, leaning her head back against the seat, closing her eyes, 'No, I don't care at all.'

He reached across to touch her, his eyes still on the

road, his face dark and unreadable but his hand warm against her face, the back of his fingers stroking down her smooth skin.

'Neither do I,' he whispered softly.

Inside his flat, she was suddenly shy, panic-stricken in fact, standing still and looking around at the sheer luxury of the place, feeling like a being from another world, lost and insignificant, not in any way part of Nick's world of wealth and confidence. In England, in her job, her familiar world around her, she had been confident, her future settled and ordinary, even able to give confidence to Bill, comfort to Nick's father, support to Chris. Here, though, in this city, in Nick's life, there had been a steady erosion of that feeling. There seemed to be clouds instead of the earth beneath her feet, only wistful longing where there had been a certainty.

'I could make us some coffee if you tell me where the kitchen is,' she said with forced brightness, turning away from his silver-eyed gaze. 'Or you could fix me a drink.'

Instead he took her bag from her suddenly nerveless fingers, putting it on the table and pulling her gently into his arms.

'You do not want a drink, Rachel,' he said quietly, 'and neither do I. This is what we both want, to touch each other, to hold each other.' He ran his hands over the slender outline of her body, his breath catching in his throat. 'God! You are so thin, so fragile,' he whispered against her hair. 'What have you been doing to yourself, child? I can't leave you for a minute and be certain that you're going to survive.'

'I couldn't eat,' she confessed against his chest, her fingers anxiously plucking at his sweater. 'I haven't been able to eat since—since . . . Oh, Nick!'

He lifted her face, cupping it in warm hands and looking into her eyes deeply before his lips at last met hers in a deep, warm, tender kiss that she could hardly believe. There was no fire between them, no burst of flame, only a deep longing and a desire to stay like that endlessly. Her arms moved around his neck and the kiss deepened as his hand moved into her hair, holding her face up to his as he held her close.

Her eyes were still closed as he swung her up into his arms and walked through the luxury that had so frightened her and into his bedroom, releasing her for a second to switch on the lamps. And then, with no further words, he began to undress her gently and slowly.

As her dress slid to the floor and his hands caressed her for a moment before moving to the clip of her bra, his eyes slowly raised to hers, an understanding in them of what he saw on her face. She was remembering the last time that she had been willing to surrender to Nick. To give him everything he wanted, and the fear of sudden and brutal rejection was a deep shadow in her eyes.

'I will not leave you, sweet Rachel,' he said thickly. 'We will love until we are too tired to touch, too tired to kiss, and then you will sleep in my arms.'

'You left me before,' she whispered, her eyes filled with a quiet acceptance that Nick should decide her fate whatever it might be. His eyes darkened at the softly spoken words. There was no fight in her, no desire to strike at him in any way, only a deep longing and a wistful plea in her face.

'Tonight is in no way the same,' he said, his lips stroking hers as he continued to unveil her. 'Tonight there is such a great difference and you want to belong to me, don't you?'

She flushed softly as he continued to undress her with delicate care, his eyes moving over her as they had done at their first meeting. But where before she had felt nothing but fear and a burning pain, she now felt warm wherever his gaze rested and when finally she stood before him, every last veil removed, he bent his head and kissed the tip of each aroused breast, his hands lightly on her hips.

'I will touch you no further if you wish it,' he murmured, his lips on the satin skin of her shoulder. 'But I know that you want to belong to me; all you have to do is say yes.'

'Yes.' She breathed the word shakily, looking into the darkened eyes that were raised to hers. He was so different, so gentle, with no trace of the savagery that she had always found in him. Tonight she had been left in no doubt of her love for him. She had realised as she had seen him in danger that she could not simply leave his life as if she had never known him; she felt as if she knew him better than she had ever known anyone. He had greeted her, too, as if there was much more than desire between them. He had left everyone to come to her, to comfort her, and her presence seemed to be a comfort to him, too.

He stood and looked down into her eyes, not moving, even though she had said so clearly that she wished to belong to him, his grey eyes reading her expression as she looked back at him. He was not yet married to Stefanie Veccetti; maybe he never would be. There was love on his face and her heart suddenly felt light and free as she smiled up at him.

'You are sure, *cara*?' he asked softly.

'I'm very sure, Nick,' she whispered, her hands moving to touch his face, a face so dear to her that her feeling showed clearly in her dark eyes.

'Then undress me,' he said with smiling tenderness, his eyes moving over her suddenly shy and blushing face. 'You are shy with me,' he murmured in delight. 'Why, Rachel? I am only like any other man. There is nothing new to discover,' he added with a gentle amusement.

He drew her hands to his waist, inviting her to begin, and she wanted to tell him that she had never seen any man before, had never stood as she stood now, naked and weak in front of anyone. But her voice had left her, her tongue refused to make the confession, and as she dropped her head, the shyness overwhelming her, he took pity on her and lifted her to the bed, his eyes laughing into hers as he performed the task himself, his golden-skinned body proud and beautiful as he looked down at her.

'Now you may hide your face, *cara*,' he assured her quietly, coming down beside her and taking her into his arms. 'Now I have you in my arms and for perhaps as long as one second I will allow you to hide from me, providing that you stay close and I can feel your loveliness tightly against me.'

But he allowed no second after all because with the touch of her body against his, his breath left him in a gasp of pleasure and he moved partly across her, lifting her face to his and capturing her mouth in a searing kiss that lit the dormant flame, banishing her shyness and turning her into a restless, tormented fire in his arms.

'Now I recognise you, Rachel!' he groaned. 'Now I know that you are the girl with hair like a flame and kisses like fire. I want you, *cara*, I want you,' he murmured, his hands hot on her skin, his heart beating above her racing heart as if there had been no pause between the last time that he had held her and this, passion flaring between them with an almost frightening

speed as they touched. Her lips moved over him as
eagerly as he caressed her, and their desire to be one
mounted within seconds, the same violent passion that
had been there since their first meeting.

'Again, I am a savage,' he muttered against her
mouth. 'I wanted to comfort you, to be gentle, but now I
only want to possess you. You take away my will-power
and my sanity,' he gasped as her arms wound around
him and her legs entwined with his, her small teeth
sinking into his shoulder as she tossed restlessly in his
arms.

Heat soared between them as they caressed, a growing
and mounting frenzy to belong to each other that
seemed to rob them of the breath to speak, and they
came together in a wild burst of passion that was like the
explosion of the universe. The sharp, searing pain that
shot through Rachel at Nick's possession was obliterated
instantly by the removal of the deep pain she had felt for
so long as her world dissolved into a golden sparkle of
stars and a warm lingering pleasure.

Her eyes opened languidly as he moved from her and
turned her to face him, and she saw his eyes, still dark
with desire, looking into hers with a sort of startled
wonder.

'You wild and crazy girl,' he whispered softly, his
hand stroking back the damp hair from her forehead.
'Why didn't you tell me? You gave me your innocence
with a fiery insistence that drove me almost mad, and I
have hurt you. You were engaged. I naturally assumed
that you were no longer a virgin. I thought you had slept
with this—this man,' he finished, seemingly a little
unsure as to what to call Chris.

'I hadn't,' she murmured, blushing hotly. 'I—I'm
not like—like that.'

And suddenly, the eyes that she had once thought cold

were laughing into hers as he pulled her fiercely into his arms.

'Not like what, Rachel?' he laughed. 'I said that we were two parts of the same flame. Does the flame only burn when I hold you? Is the fire only for me? I know what you are like. I am still a million miles into the air with the glory of it, but I never meant to hurt you.'

'I'm quite all right,' she said demurely, her eyes avoiding his, and he tilted her face to his kisses, smiling into her eyes.

'Then if you are,' he threatened softly, 'I can safely make love to you again. I would not know what to do with my life if the fire went out; I could never let you go.'

It was almost a promise. She had made no secret of her love; he had seen it clearly on her face and now he had no doubts, but he had confessed nothing except a constant and burning desire. But he had been gentle, tender, and his hands were caressing her tenderly now. She moved against him, content. He cared about her and she would fight to keep him in any way that was necessary.

CHAPTER NINE

RACHEL stirred, not opening her eyes. She had no need to look around her to realise where she was—the langour of her own body told her, the brimming happiness inside her—and she stretched slowly, her limbs moving luxuriously against the silken sheets.

A murmur of laughter had her opening her eyes quickly to find Nick crouched by the bed, already showered and dressed, his sparkling eyes on her sleepy contented face.

'You're dressed!' she exclaimed. 'Is it late?'

'Ten o'clock,' he informed her, adding, when she gasped in surprise and made a quick move, 'No need to panic. It is Sunday, remember? No work, no problems. We have the whole day to be together with no interruptions from the rest of the world.'

She settled back against the pillows, smiling up at him, and he stood and looked down at her for a second, a little smile on his lips.

'I am about to prepare breakfast and, that being the case, I see no reason why you should lie there so comfortably any longer. Out, and into the shower, lazybones!' He dived at the bed and swept the sheets from her, pulling her to her feet and catching her in his arms as she squealed in surprise and annoyance. 'On the other hand,' he added softly as he felt her slim body against his, 'breakfast is perhaps not as appealing as it seemed to be a moment ago. Maybe you are in the right place after all.' He cupped her winsome face in his hands and brushed her lips with his and her hands came up of their own volition to caress the silken rasp of his face.

155

'Rachel,' he murmured softly, muttering then quiet words in Italian that she wished so much she could understand.

The shrill ringing of the telephone in the other room brought them both back speedily from the world they were drifting into and Nick looked ruefully into her eyes.

'I suppose we must eat after all. Neither of us ate last night and you need to be fed regularly by the feel of you.' He tossed her his bathrobe as he moved to answer the insistent ringing. 'Shower quickly and we will eat. Then, we will see,' he finished, his eyes sweeping over her as he strode out.

Rachel tied the robe around her and wandered to the mirror. For the first time in her life she felt beautiful, and her own face astonished her. There was love in it and a deep contentment, a sweet soft look to her mouth, an enchantment in her eyes that spoke openly of a woman in love. She felt more assured than she had ever felt, more alive, hardly able to stop looking at her own image and the utter peace that she saw on her face.

'You could not have chosen a worse time to ring me!'

It suddenly dawned on her that Nick was speaking in English, probably, she mused, because he had been using the language for most of the night as they talked and made love. He was comfortable in the language and she realised that he probably did not even know that he was speaking it. The smile of amusement faded from her face however at his next words.

'Stefanie! Sunday morning at ten o'clock is not my idea of a good time to discuss wedding arrangements! I had not the faintest idea that you were arriving today.' He sighed loudly and angrily as he listened for a moment and then said tersely, 'Very well, I will collect you and spare you one hour and no more. My day is planned and I have no intention of altering my plans. You can go to my father as he is in Rome with Toni.' He suddenly

dropped into Italian. Whether or not he had suddenly
realised that he was speaking in English, or whether
Stefanie Veccetti had complained, Rachel did not know.
She didn't want to hear anything else and she wished
bitterly that he had spoken in his own language all the
time. She didn't want to be pulled back from her
happiness, to be made to face the hard reality of her
relationship with Nick.

She almost ran into the bathroom, locking the door
and switching on the shower. If Nick came back and saw
her still in the bedroom he would almost certainly realise
that she had heard, and if he explained to her about his
future wife she would die.

She stood in the middle of the floor fighting tears,
realising that he had never expressed any other feeling
than desire. He had made her no promises in the long
and passion-filled night. All the dreams had been hers,
and now she was what he had always wanted her to be,
his mistress, living in a flat that he paid for, no doubt to
stay there after his maraige while Stefanie Veccetti lived
in the house that he would build on the hill. He would
come to her when he could, bring her here, too, to this
flat, but his wife would be with him everywhere else; he
had not altered his plans at all. Stephanie was suitable,
wealthy and polished, a perfect wife for Nick Orsiani.

'Rachel!' His call and his quick tap on the door had
her anxiously looking around. 'Why have you locked the
door?' he asked impatiently, rattling the knob. 'Let me
in, I want to talk to you. '

She went to the door and opened it and he looked at
her in surprise, seeing her still tightly wrapped in his
robe, although he could hear the constant running of the
shower.

'You intend to shower in my robe?' he asked,
laughing down at her. 'I object!'

'I—I was just seeing if the water was hot. I'm sorry, I'm wasting it.' She moved to turn off the shower but he caught her to him.

'Leave it, there is a constant supply of hot water. Waste it all you want, drain every last drop of water in Rome if you like, but don't lock yourself in. When you didn't answer straight away I had visions of you lying under the shower having slipped and knocked yourself out. You worry me constantly, *cara*.'

He tilted her face to his and kissed her, smiling into her eyes, apparently not noticing the growing misery that she was at pains to conceal.

'I have to go out and you will have to get your own breakfast. I will be just over an hour, even, if I am unlucky, two hours. There is everything here that you need. Stay here in the flat, Rachel. Don't leave it. I want to go out and know that you are safely here. I will be back as soon as I can and then we have the rest of the day to plan. I need to talk to you.'

The rest of the day! Nick was meeting his future wife to plan the rest of his life. She threw her arms around his neck and clung to him fiercely, knowing that it would be for the last time. There was no way that she could stay here in Rome now. She loved him too much, needed his love, and only a clean and complete break would allow her to survive. Her lips sought his cheek in a last goodbye kiss and he urgently found her mouth, kissing her with stinging sweetness, holding her tightly.

'Anyone but a lunatic would have had enough love for days after last night,' he whispered huskily, 'but I am clearly a lunatic. You look at me and I want you, you touch me and I am desperate. Eat your breakfast and wait for me. I will hurry back.'

She dived under the shower as he left, tying her hair in a towel to keep it dry. It was too long and thick to dry speedily and she had so little time, two hours at the most, in fact, to get out of Nick's life for ever. Within fifteen minutes she had called a taxi and was heading across the city to her own flat, anxiously looking at her watch, willing the speeding cab to go faster, steadfastly not thinking about anything except the need to disappear completely.

She bundled things into her suitcases, hastily counting the money that she had in the flat. She could give a cheque for her air fare and her salary had been paid into the bank in England, as had everyone else's. She would have a little money to last until she could find another job, more than she would have had if Nick had not been paying her rent here, she realised with a quick pang of regret. She knew with a deep certainty that he would come for her. He had said it on the night that Chris had appeared at her flat and now she was more certain than ever.

A sudden deep surge of feeling had her hesitating, almost ready to stay here and be anything that he wanted. He needed her as she needed him, she never doubted that, except that she loved him and his feelings for her were only desire. He had never pretended otherwise and the words that he had whispered to her during the long night had been words of passion, not love. He had not thought it necessary to mention Stefanie at all.

She didn't even imagine that he loved Stefanie Veccetti, but she had seen his eyes when he had risen from his desk to greet the small and exquisitely dressed woman. There had been a glad surprise, the look of equals meeting, a certainty on his face. They would be a well-matched couple, while she knew that she was only a frenzied dream to Nick, someone he wanted with a savage determination. Such feelings burned themselves out.

Her decision to go to the airport on the off chance of a

flight paid off because a cancellation had left one seat
vacant on the flight to London and she took it. She dared
not linger in Rome now the two hours were up; Nick
would be searching for her. The thought of his shock,
his possible hurt and his anger brought tears to her eyes,
but she boarded the plane with a wooden expression on
her face and a cold, lost feeling inside, only asking
herself when the aircraft was clear of the ground what
she was going to do with the rest of her life.

Rachel stayed overnight in London, finding the
cheapest hotel that she could and trying to gather her
thoughts to the present and her situation. There was no
way that she could go home. Nick would come there.
The firm had her address and the people there knew her
too well; she had lived in the same place for the whole of
her life and her trail would be simple enough for a child
to follow.

In the morning she scanned the papers, trying to put
some enthusiasm into what she was doing but finding
her mind wandering again and again away from the long
columns of possible vacancies, away from the grey
morning light of the city and back to Rome, to the
sunshine, the gaiety and to Nick.

Every dark head she saw brought a quick burst of
excitement to her and she realised that it would take a
very long time for her mind to be able to even begin to
adjust to a life that did not and could never contain Nick.

For a little over two weeks she stayed in London,
taking temporary jobs as a typist, but the pay was not
what she was used to and living was very expensive in
the city. She was rapidly forced to the conclusion that if
she was to survive and still have money enough to live
away from home she would have to settle into a
permanent post. She moved north, as far from her old
home as she felt was necessary, and after a week she had
success.

'You seem to have good qualifications, Miss Gordon.'
Little eyes peered at her suspiciously from behind thick
spectacles. 'I have been wondering why you are not
employed at the moment.'

Mr Stockley was a country solicitor and she had
applied for the post of secretary with few hopes of
success, but it seemed that he was in urgent need of
someone and he had telephoned the little hotel where she
was staying on the same day that he had received her
application.

'I've been working in Italy, as you can see from my
application,' she said, trying to remember what she used
to be like in the days when she had been efficient and
quick-tempered, before Nick had softened her into her
present state, trying to get the same brisk tone to her
voice. Apparently she succeeded because he let that
particular theme go.

'Of course I did ask for references,' he reminded her,
looking at her severely over his spectacles. 'I have the
remarks of your secretarial college but that is quite a
long time ago. I need some kind of reference from your
last employer.'

'Yes. Well, as I stated on my application form, Mr
Stockley, I worked for the same firm from leaving school
and then they—they closed,' she finished, crossing her
fingers mentally. It certainly wouldn't do to say that
they had been absorbed by Orsiani Italia. 'I went to Italy
then and I've just come back.'

He looked doubtfully at her pale face but appeared to
find some lingering traces of tan and nodded.

'Well, that will be quite all right, Miss Gordon. Just
give me the name of the Italian firm and I will write to
them.'

For a second she almost shouted 'No!' but she caught
herself in time. Nick would be out on the next flight and
her hiding would be to no avail because she never

doubted that once he touched her she would do anything he asked.

'You may start, however,' he was adding grudgingly. 'I need someone at once and yours is the best application. There is just the matter of the reference.'

He pushed a pad across the desk at her and she tried to gather her scattered wits. Of course she had known that it would be a difficulty and she had been relying on the distance to Italy putting everyone off the idea of writing for any reference. Mr Stockley was not a man to be put off. Her mind searched wildly through Rome for a name, any name, and she almost burst into laughter as she found one, praying that the rather dusty little man in the thick spectacles was not an ardent tourist.

'Trevi,' she said firmly, writing it down. 'They make those very expensive clothes that come from Italy, you know.' He didn't know, clearly, and her confidence grew. 'Via Condotti, Rome,' she added, writing the address. Oh, Toni, bless you, her mind whispered as she pushed the pad brightly back to Mr Stockley. With any luck, it would be months before the letter came back to him, address unknown, and then he might have decided not to bother anyway. Certainly when it reached its destination someone would realise that it was a joke; maybe, with any luck, they would throw it into the fountain and it would be lost. She needed time to gather herself together, time to build up her depleted resources, and this was the only way.

'I see that you gave as your address the Wheatsheaf,' he observed, leaning back and taking on the air of her employer now that his suspicions were stilled. 'Do you intend to stay there?'

'Oh, no!' She smiled. 'It would be too expensive. I'll have to try and find somewhere else now that I can settle in the area.'

He gave a little nod of satisfaction at her good sense in

realising that the rather poor little hotel was beyond her means and she felt a quick flare of her old temper, wondering if all men had to have this feeling that lowly employees should remain lowly.

'I seem to remember seeing a cottage to let,' he muttered, reaching behind him into the muddle that seemed to be his filing system. 'Ah, yes, here it is.' He peered at the morning paper, handing it to her, his stubby little finger on the place. 'You could copy that and perhaps enquire?' he suggested, making it quite clear that the paper was his and not to be borrowed. She copied it and thanked him. She had the afternoon in which to look for it and, if the price was right, then she could begin to make a place for herself here. Beyond that she would not think; beyond that was a long future stretching into emptiness.

It was raining—again! Rachel trudged down the road to the cottage, her head down to escape the drizzle that had seemed to last like her tears since she had left Rome over two months ago. She pushed her cold hands into the pockets of her yellow cagoule, watching her feet as they walked through the damp fallen leaves that littered the lane, seeing that the bottom of the legs of her jeans were wet. It would have been easy to just go into the dismal little cottage that she had rented and close the door, go to sleep and stay there for ever. There seemed to be no end to her unhappiness, and now her new problem was the latest in a series of disasters that seemed to her at the moment to have made up her whole life.

She had needed time to gather herself together when she had given the false address to Mr Stockley, time to enlarge her very seriously depleted resources. It had given her exactly six weeks before the letter returned with stamp marks from what appeared to be every Italian post office, and Mr Stockley held it accusingly before her eyes as she went into the office.

'It is quite clear from your skill and your ability that you have indeed been a private secretary, Miss Gordon,' he said sharply, going so far as to stand up to emphasise his point. 'But you have also been willing to practise deceit! There is no such place as Trevi.'

Oh, but there is, she wanted to say. It's a glittering fountain that takes your money and promises you happiness and tells you lies. She wanted to tell him that it was in a sunny land, a warm land where Nick lived, a place she would never see again, but she said nothing. She was so used to taking blows now that it didn't seem to matter.

'I must have absolute faith in anyone that I employ,' he added starchily. 'I shudder to think of the confidential matters that you have dealt with during your six weeks here. I certainly cannot continue to employ you.' A sudden alarming thought seemed to strike him that made him ask with horror, 'Have you been in prison?'

'Not yet, Mr Stockley, give me time,' she said wearily, reaching for her cagoule that hung on the old-fashioned coat hook behind the door and slipping it on over her head.

'I'm sorry,' he said as a rather harsh afterthought.

'It really doesn't matter,' Rachel said dully. 'I would have had to leave soon anyway. I'm pregnant.'

She didn't say it to shock the stuffy little man, although it certainly did do that. She merely voiced aloud what she had known inside for a couple of weeks: she was going to have Nick's baby. She slung her bag over her shoulder and walked out into the quiet street with no further comment.

Now, having left the bus at the end of the lane, she walked with lonely steps to her dismal retreat, her steps silent on the wet leaves, her head bent against the rain, her hood well down and nothing in her mind except misery.

She didn't even know that a car was outside the cottage until she heard the slam of the door and her head shot up in alarmed surprise, a feeling that turned into a mixture of wild happiness and cold fear as she saw Nick standing beside a long dark car, his grey eyes watching her angrily.

'Do not attempt to run,' he grated as she came to a halt. 'I would chase you and catch you but it would not improve my temper. Come here!'

She had little alternative and she went slowly with a mixture of reluctance and excitement, her steps dragging, to his obvious annoyance, until she looked up into his angry eyes.

'You found me,' she said uneasily as he towered over her but never touched her.

'Ah! So you knew that I would continue with the game of hide and seek that seems to occupy your mind to the exclusion of everything else!' he snapped. 'Yes, I found you, or, to be more precise, several firms of inquiry agents and I found you. And this, I take it,' he added scathingly, 'is the hole to which you ran.'

His eyes turned on the dejected-looking little cottage and then back to her as she stood wet and oddly defenceless in front of him.

'There—there was nowhere else to go,' she whispered and he muttered in exasperation, grasping her arm with hard fingers and turning her to the cottage.

'Well, as I am here and as you are here, we may as well go inside. Certainly I do not intend to stand here until I am soaked to the skin by this endless rain.'

His impatience was very much in evidence as she searched in the muddle of her bag for her key to the cottage, and his quiet blast of Italian as he saw the interior had her cringing.

'You can come into the sitting-room,' she offered in a rather scared voice as he stood in the doorway and looked round in growing anger.

'You overwhelm me,' he rasped, walking into the miserable little room that answered loosely to that name, a further explosion of Italian escaping him as he saw the dull and dingy room, felt the cold and damp of the place that was almost as bad as being outside.

'I take it that you sleep on the floor?' he enquired sarcastically. 'And by the look of you,' he added as she removed her cagoule and straightened her brown sweater, 'you live mainly on bread and water.'

'What do you want, Nick?' she asked quietly, turning away to look through the window at the pouring rain.

'What do you imagine I want?' he rasped. 'I have come for you, as you obviously knew that I would.'

'I didn't think that you'd be able to find me,' she whispered almost to herself. 'I didn't want you to find me.'

'So it would seem,' he remarked sharply. 'I could not leave Italy for some time and in any case, after an immediate investigation had shown that you had not returned to your home, there seemed to be little that I could do, except perhaps to travel around England shouting your name at the top of my voice. I decided to call in a few experts, six as it turned out, and they have searched for you, but you have remained hidden very successfully until this week.'

'I—I can't see how you found me,' she said quietly, afraid to turn and look at him.

'Your bank,' he told her in an irritated voice. 'I cannot think why I never thought of that at first,' he added in self-disgust.

'They had no business to tell you,' she observed crossly, turning to look at him and as quickly looking away at the angry look in his eyes.

'They refused to tell the inquiry agents,' he confessed, adding in an arrogant tone, 'it was only when I was able to get here to England myself that they relented.'

'When they realised who you were and that you were rolling in money,' she said sarcastically.

'I do not make a habit of rolling in it and in any case it was not that which made them relent. I told them that you were a little strange at times and might be in danger. I pointed out that it would not look good for the bank to have your address and refuse to give it. The newspapers would make a great deal of it if anything happened to you.'

'You—you ...' she stared at him speechlessly. 'You had no right ...'

'I had every right!' he snapped. 'I needed to find you and nothing was going to stop me. Nothing will ever stop me,' he added with a savage emphasis. 'And now that we have completed this pointless discussion, you will pack your things and we will get out of this place before we both develop some unpleasant illness, although by the look of you, I have arrived two months too late to safeguard your health.'

'I'm not going anywhere,' she said quietly and with what he obviously took to be a subborn look, because he seemed about to explode with rage.

'How many things in this room belong to you?' he enquired sharply, looking round with distaste.

'Nothing, but ...'

'I am very relieved to hear it,' he grated, turning to the door and striding toward the stairs.

'Where are you going?' She ran after him anxiously but he never even bothered to look round and when she arrived astonished and breathless in her bedroom, he was already throwing things into her suitcases with utter abandon and some real degree of savagery.

'I'm not leaving here!' she shouted, only to be ignored
as he swept the things from the dressing-table with one
angry movement of his hand, pushing them into her case
with more force than concern for the final result. It was
like watching a powerful machine out of control and
Rachel felt a strange and unwelcome surge of relief that
she would not get the chance to defy him. Angry he may
be, furious even, but she felt safer than she had done
since she had boarded the flight from Italy.

One last look around the room and he was lifting the
cases and striding back to the front door of the cottage,
out into the rain, and before Rachel had even arrived at
the foot of the stairs, her suitcases were in the boot of his
car and the lid slammed shut.

'If there is anything here that belongs to you, you
have one minute to claim it,' he informed her, standing
in the hall and filling it, it seemed, and when she just
looked at him in stunned silence he pushed her still wet
cagoule into her hands and picked up the key of the
cottage that she had dropped on to a table. 'Very well, I
take your silence to mean that you now have all your
possessions and that nothing in the kitchen belongs to
you.'

'It's a furnished cottage,' she muttered, getting into
her cagoule as there appeared to be no alternative,
suddenly too tired to argue.

'Really?' he remarked sarcastically. 'I would say that
it is flying false colours. Your flat in Rome is furnished,
if you are able to cast your mind back to it and make a
comparison!'

'I don't really care where I live,' she sighed wearily,
standing forlornly in the rain as he locked the door.

'I do care!' he snapped, looking at the key in his hand
as if he was considering throwing it into the bushes, but
clearly thinking better of it. He took her arm in a biting
grasp and marched her to the car.

She was still in a daze. It seemed that minutes ago she had been walking down the wet lane filled with despair, with no future before her, and now she was in a luxurious car, a very angry man beside her, her affairs ruthlessly dealt with and her destination unknown. She wasn't going to Rome, she was certain of that, no matter what Nick said or did. He may be able to manhandle her out of an isolated cottage and into his car but he could not force her on to a plane and back into his life.

'You're wasting your time, Nick,' she observed quietly. 'I don't know what your plans are, but ...'

'You know damned well what my plans are!' he snapped, not looking at her at all.

'I'll not live in Rome with you. I'll not have you being ...'

'Being what?' he snarled, in a greater rage than she had seen for some time. 'Your lover? If you will cast your mind back, you will undoubtedly remember that I am already your lover, in no uncertain terms. It was not necessary either to force my attentions on you. You may now look ill, wet and more than a little bedraggled, but two months ago you were burning in my arms and half the fire was coming from you!' He turned his head to glare at her with stormy eyes. 'The fact that you ran away then, no doubt regretting that even as I left my flat you were still more than willing to be in my arms, has nothing to do with the matter. You now belong to me and I have come to collect you.' He turned his attention back to the wet road and she never answered. She hadn't run away because she regretted it. She would never regret it; it had been the happiest time of her life.

'Where have you been working?' he asked a little more quietly in a few minutes.

'For a solicitor in the town,' she answered briefly.

'Then why were you back at that miserable cottage so soon?' he asked with a degree of suspicion.

'I got the sack this morning,' she told him and then, seeing his look of puzzlement and remembering how he had taken her words before at their face value, she added, 'I was dismissed.'

'You? Dismissed?' His real astonishment gave her a sudden little glow. He looked as if he thought that anyone would have to be mad to give her the sack and it was worth any written testimonial, coming from Nick.

'Your work is excellent and you are supremely efficient,' he said, adding to her glow. 'How many worked in the offices?' he suddenly asked, suspicion entering his voice again.

'Not offices, office,' she told him quietly. 'I worked there and no one else, except Mr Stockley, the boss.'

'He was making advances to you and you used your sharp little tongue against him?' he demanded to know, suddenly very annoyed again. 'Is that why you were dismissed?'

'No,' she said with the first feeling of laughter in her for weeks at the idea of the stuffy little solicitor making advances to her. 'I gave a false address for references. He found out.' She paused a minute and then said almost to herself, the idea now annoying her, 'He asked me if I'd been in prison!'

For a second she thought that Nick was going to laugh, but he didn't, although his temper had subsided again.

'So, as your faithful lover, what do you want me to do? Go round after lunch and beat him up or congratulate him on being able to see into the future?' he enquiried sardonically, adding as an afterthought, 'Though I imagine that I will be the one to end up in prison, the provocation I am expected to suffer!'

'I really pity you,' she said with an edge of anger to her voice. 'You must find life really difficult.'

'Pity,' he stressed darkly, 'is not what I intend to have

from you. Here we are,' he added, before she could do more than gasp at his words.

They were slowing in front of a picturesque little inn and Nick drove round the back to an old-fashioned courtyard, parking and then helping her out.

'We will get your luggage in a minute,' he assured her. 'First, I want you into the warmth, and fed reasonably fast.'

'If this is where you're staying,' she ventured, 'hasn't it occurred to you that they may not have a room free for me?'

'We are booked into the only double room with a sitting-room that the little place boasts,' he said firmly and she was inside before she could catch her breath.

It was warm and cosy, still looking several hundred years old, but certainly warmed by central heating, and Rachel suddenly realised that she had felt cold for days. There was already a buffet in the centre of the main room, and as it was of considerable size, it looked as if they expected plenty of diners, although there was nobody there as yet. The smell from the kitchen also told her that it was probably a popular eating place with the local people and she wondered in a little panic if Mr Stockley came here, dismissing the idea at once in relief. It looked too expensive; he wouldn't come here. She didn't fancy having him speak to her and hearing him get the sharp edge of Nick's tongue in front of other diners.

'Mr Orsiani!' This weather! I don't know how you're able to stand it after coming from a place like Italy.'

A jolly little woman rounded the edge of the bar and came towards them, her beaming face dimpled and kindly, and Nick smiled down at her in an unusually pleasant manner.

'I'm managing very badly, Mrs Prestwick, and very glad to be back into this civilised place. Did you have the fire lit in my sitting-room as I asked?'

'An hour ago, Mr Orsiani.' She beamed at him. 'I've just this minute been to look and it's glowing nicely, warm as toast. You'll not be cold in there, not with the central heating as well.'

'My wife needs to be kept warm,' Nick said smoothly. 'I think, too, that we will eat upstairs if you can manage it. She has been ill, as you can see, and I doubt if she could face a dining-room full of people.'

'She's very pale.' The little woman peered at Rachel and so did Nick, and then they looked at each other like consultant surgeons about to discuss the possible treatment. 'We can easily serve your lunch in your room. She can eat in front of the fire.'

'Good,' Nick remarked, even going so far as to pull her cagoule hood from her head and smooth the damp tendrils of hair from her face. He was treating her like a wet cat who had been found outside. Get the maid to give her a quick scrub down and then she can crouch in front of the fire. Rachel's eyes were beginning to lose their blank, defeated look and Nick looked down at her with a sudden gleam in his eyes as he saw the danger signals.

'What would she fancy eating?' the kindly hostess asked and Rachel blossomed into sound.

'From the delightful smell coming from the kitchen I imagine that there is to be roast beef. I would like that, please,' she said in a clear voice, and the little face in front of her went red with embarrassment and then creased with laughter.

'Well, here I've been thinking you were Italian and didn't speak English. You must think I'm daft.' She was laughing heartily and Rachel smiled serenely.

'Of course not,' she assured her. 'I thought, though, that I had better speak, in case you got the impression that I was. Mr Orsiani is a very well-known practical joker,' she added smugly, causing Nick to get a quick look of wary surprise from the woman. 'He will eat what I eat. Roast beef and all the trimmings.'

'Give us about fifteen minutes,' Nick said firmly, taking Rachel's arm and getting control of the situation again, and then he was leading her upstairs, having given his car keys to the porter and arranged for Rachel's luggage to be sent up at the same time as the meal.

CHAPTER TEN

ONCE inside the old and cosy room upstairs, Nick turned to her purposefully.

'Now we will remove that dripping piece of plastic that you are wearing.' He had the cagoule from her and strode off with it before she could protest, coming back in seconds with his all-too-familiar bathrobe.

'Get those damp clothes off and wrap yourself in this,' he ordered, towering over her grimly, reaching out towards her when she made no move to obey.

'I have no intention whatever of staying!' she snapped, moving out of reach, still annoyed at being treated like an idiot downstairs. 'And as to changing, I'm perfectly dry.'

'I'm glad to see that you are looking better,' he said, his lips quirking. 'Adrenalin gives a quick boost to the body and does little harm.'

'Especially when it can be used up by delivering a quick kick to the shins!' she retorted, turning away, two bright spots of colour on her face. She didn't feel much better, in fact. It was all too easy to allow Nick to sweep her along, to fit into his plans. It was impossible to look at him and deny him anything, but there was no way that she would be prepared to go back to Rome to live with him, to see him married to someone else, to know that any time between them was stolen time. Surrendering to him now seemed to have been a fit of madness, although it seemed less like that when he looked at her.

'Get those damp things off, Rachel,' he ordered quietly enough, his hand coming to her shoulder.

She spun round at him angrily, not wanting him to touch her when soon he would be holding somebody else in his arms—frequently did, she reminded herself painfully.

'I'm staying exactly as I am! I'll eat with you and then I'm going!'

'And that is your final decision?' he asked, his eyes beginning to sparkle with anger, little of the silent amusement left.

'Yes!' She turned away and was suddenly swept off her feet as Nick scooped her up and set her none too gently in one of the big chairs by the fire.

'First, the weapons, in case you decide to try and carry out your idea of attacking me,' he stated grimly, pulling off her wet shoes. 'And now, the damp clothes!'

'What do you think you're doing?' she shrieked as he hauled her to her feet, his hands at the zip of her jeans.

He didn't even bother to answer but slapped her frantic hands away and completed his task of unzipping the jeans and hauling them off ungently so that she fell back into the chair.

'You—you uncouth monster!' she choked in embarrassment as her tights joined the crumpled jeans on the floor.

'Later!' he rasped, pulling her back to her feet and reaching for her jumper, ducking easily as she lashed out at him in a rage.

'There is no need to look so maidenly,' he growled as she stood in bra and brief panties, shocked and angry, her hair in disarray, her cheeks pink with confusion. 'I have seen this film before—several times,' he added, pushing her into the bathrobe and leaving her to tie it close with unsteady fingers. 'Now you may curl up in front of the fire. I will dispose of these and change into dry clothes myself with an easier mind. You will feel less

inclined in your present state of dress to race out into the
road as soon as my back is turned and beg a lift from the
first passing motorist!'

It had seriously crossed her mind, and his angry
glance at her face, his raised eyebrow, showed her that as
usual he had been one jump ahead of her.

He was back soon in doeskin trousers and a black
high-necked sweater with expensive shoes on his feet,
and looking so handsome, so Italian and so angry that
she looked away into the blaze of the fire, her feet curled
under her like a child.

'Good,' he stated in a hard voice. 'We will now eat. All
explanations of your conduct can wait until later.'

She looked up to ask him angrily how he dared to talk
like this, treating her like a runaway wife as if he had
every right to come and capture her, but the rattle of a
trolley at the door and his hard look of warning silenced
her before she had said even one word.

The laden trolley was wheeled in by the cheerful
woman from downstairs. She had clearly decided to deal
with this important guest herself, and Rachel recognised
her awe. Nobody had to state that Nick was wealthy and
important, he just looked it, and as she opened the flaps
of the trolley to turn it into a small table with white
cloth, setting out the cutlery deftly, the pleasure on the
face of the little woman was almost solely pride that she
had managed to get such a man into her small and cosy
inn.

'There!' she said with satisfaction, standing back to
beam at them both. 'Roast beef with all the trimmings
and apple pie with cream to follow. Those chairs by the
wall will fit nicely to the trolley, Mr Orsiani, and when
you've finished, just push the whole thing outside where
we can get it. Nobody need trouble you further then.'

'When we have consumed this we may not have the

energy to move the trolley,' he pleased her by saying, and then she was gone and Nick was motioning Rachel into one of the chairs he had carried forward.

The fire was blazing, the rain was pouring down the windows and Nick sat opposite in silence, serving her first, his movements economical and graceful as she sat with lowered lashes watching his capable brown hands.

'Eat,' he growled softly, his eyes glancing at her flushed cheeks, holding her gaze for a second as she looked up. There was an instant flare of feeling that shot between them like a flash of light, darkening his eyes and bringing a swift streak of colour to his high cheekbones, but it was Rachel who looked down speedily, her trembling hands reaching for her knife and fork, and he said nothing else.

They ate in total silence, a silence that grew more taut and deep as the meal progressed until the atmosphere between them was singing with intensity, like the build-up of an electrical storm, and Rachel's breath was tight in her chest.

He stood smoothly as they finished, and poured her coffee, placing it beside the big deep chair that flanked the blazing fire, taking his own to the opposite side of the fireplace and wheeling the trolley through the door into the passage.

He came back in and moved the small chairs back to the place by the wall and then went with deliberate steps and locked the door, not looking at her at all until he was once more facing her across the soft woollen rug that stretched cosily in front of the fire.

'Why did you leave me?' he asked quietly, his eyes on her downcast face.

He waited for her answer but there was nothing that she was prepared to say. What could she say? That she had stayed with him because she loved him and had forgotten in the glory of it that he was not and never could be hers? That she had been so desperately frightened when he almost died that she had cast all thoughts aside in her desire to be close to him? There was his marriage and he knew it. He only expected her to be his mistress, to live with him in the bursts of passion that would rule their lives for a while and then to part in a friendly manner by mutual agreement. That was not how she had lived her life before Nick had entered it so violently, and she could not live it like that now.

'When I came back and found that you had gone,' he said with a quietness that she could hardly believe when she remained silent, 'I went crazy. I tore round to your flat but you had so clearly left Rome.' He was silent for a moment but she dared not look up. 'For a while, for a few hateful minutes,' he continued softly, 'I thought that you had been fooling me after all, that you had been willing to go to any lengths to pay me back for separating you from that irresponsible boy. I knew what I had heard you tell him, I knew that you no longer imagined yourself to be in love with him, but I knew also your anger and the way you had lashed out at me before.' There was a taut and almost pain-filled sound to his voice, but she refused to look up and meet his grey eyes, knowing that it would take very little to have her flying across into his arms, and she could never afford that luxury again.

'Then I remembered the look on your face when I nearly crashed the helicopter. I remembered you in my arms and the way you gave me what you had given no other man, and my doubts faded and left me with only an impossible puzzle and the urgent need to find you. Why did you leave me when you love me so much, Rachel?' he finished quietly, making her lift her face in startled anxiety to meet his clear silver gaze.

'I don't!' Her tongue sprang to her defence automatically but he smiled slowly, his eyes moving over her flushed face.

'You are not a girl who becomes a mistress to anyone,' he observed softly, his eyes holding hers. 'Even with a fiancé and a wedding arranged, you were still innocent. But you gave yourself to me and the look on your face was not merely one of passion. I could not leave Rome immediately to find you but I knew that wherever you were, you belonged to me. I would not have waited so patiently to fulfil my obligations had I known the circumstances you were living in,' he added deeply.

'You waited long enough!' she suddenly cried out in a burst of anguish, knowing why he had not been free to come before, no longer bothering to deny her love. 'I suppose the wedding is over now and things happily settled.'

'Ah, so you knew about the wedding?' he asked with little surprise. 'I might have known that the supposed secret was in fact the talk of the offices.' He paused a second and looked at her now bent head. 'I would have thought that you would have told me that little snippet of information,' he added softly. 'We did a lot of talking that night and yet you still kept that secretly to yourself.' He sounded hurt that she had not in fact completely bared her soul to him and she could hardly believe her ears. 'Do you intend to go on keeping little things hidden from me?' he finished.

'Little things!' She was suddenly wildly angry, indescribably hurt that he could take this attitude. 'What do you suggest would have been a good way to tell you? I could perhaps have simply blurted it out. ''By the way, Nick, darling, I understand that you're getting married?'' I can imagine myself looking up into your eyes and saying that! You cold-blooded monster!'

'Me!' He sat bolt upright in his chair and stared at her. 'That is why you left me?' he asked softly. 'You thought that I was about to marry and that I was, even so, willing to take everything you gave me? Oh, Rachel!'

He sounded so quietly disappointed in her that she stared at him in astonishment, unwilling to let the tiny leap of her heart take any firm grip.

'But—but you and Princess Veccetti . . .'

'Thank you so much,' he said with quiet mockery. 'She is beautiful, but a little too old for me, I think. She has the best attention that money can buy. She is very well cared for, better than I have so far managed to care for you. But apart from the fact that I do not fancy her in the slightest, my father would object strongly to his son marrying the woman who has become the love of his later years. I was not even invited to accompany him on his honeymoon to Capri,' he finished with a look of mockery and delight on his face that had her staring at him open-mouthed. 'Just then,' he added, his eyes darkening, 'you called me darling. You have not done that before. It took a long time even to get you to use my name. I hope that I shall hear you call me darling again, very often.'

Only Nick seemed to have this ability to leave her open-mouthed, and she still could not believe it. Vincenzo Orsiani and the woman who had seemed to be destined for Nick! She remembered his disappointment when the woman whom Rachel had imagined would be his daughter-in-law had not come to the villa, she remembered his face clearly now on the couple of occasions that her name had been mentioned, and she remembered her own realisation that he was still a very attractive man. A little of her old anger gripped her and she glared at Nick in annoyance.

'You let me believe . . .'

'That I was interested in Stefanie?' he interrupted softly. 'You seemed determined to believe the worst of me and you seemed to be still playing your game. If by continuing the game I could keep you in Rome, then I was prepared to do it. Anything I have to do to keep you, I will always do.' He leaned back in his chair, his eyes on her face. 'Marry me, Rachel,' he said into the quiet, and the shock of it, the knowledge of the answer she would have to give, had her springing up and walking away to look out of the window at the weeping rain.

'I can't!' she cried bitterly. 'You won't want to anyway.'

'I have just asked you,' he said quietly, apparently still sitting where he was, no anger in his voice.

'Except you weren't in possession of all the facts,' she choked, tears blurring her eyes. 'I'm pregnant and I know what men think of that. I'll be ugly and fat and no further use to you. I won't!'

He said nothing and she realised that she had been right. He was shocked and no doubt disappointed, and she tried to think of a way to get him out of it all. She had to try to get him out of this embarrassing situation but she couldn't think of anything. She was too deeply mixed up and unhappy to try to even begin thinking clearly.

His arms came round her from behind and she stiffened like a frightened colt.

'This is what you think, my foolish Rachel?' he asked softly. 'Is this why your father was supposed to have walked out and left?'

'It *is* why he left!' she cried, trying to keep as far away from him as possible, not wanting to feel the waves of pleasure that raced over her. 'You needn't feel guilty, Nick. I—I wanted to make love as much as you. You're not responsible.'

'I'd better be!' he exclaimed violently, spinning her round to face him, relenting when he saw her unhappy face. 'Oh, Rachel,' he said softly, cupping her face in warm hands. 'What you do not know about men would fill a whole library. Your father may have left for that reason, but I very much doubt it. He left more likely because he had never really loved your mother, just as you never really loved that stupid boy.'

'I'm not so foolish that I haven't fathomed that out for myself,' she said unhappily, avoiding his eyes by closing her own. 'But the same thing applies. You don't love me, Nick. You only want me, and that's not going to be enough now.'

'Come here,' he said quietly, leading her back to the fire, sitting in the chair he had left and pulling her into it with him. 'You don't know that I have known you for far longer than you have known me, do you?' He held her close, comforting and warm, in no way desiring, and she relaxed a little against him. 'My father came back from England,' he continued, 'singing your praises until Toni and I were utterly sick of hearing your name. The saintly Rachel became a bore of the first order, his party piece, much repeated. Then, when he retired, in his usual methodical way, he went through everything with me. I was already running the place but every last item had to be seen to, including the staff files. That was when I saw you for the first time, over a year ago.'

He tilted her chin and dropped a kiss on her nose, right at the tip as if she was a treasured child.

'My father suddenly let out a great roar and said, "That's her! That's Rachel!" and I thought, my God, not again! Seconds later I was staring at your face. The little staff photograph was in black and white like all the rest but I was stunned by the feeling that it gave me. I became obsessed. I found myself growing jealous when he spoke of you, I found myself sneaking the photograph away to have it enlarged, I found myself looking at it when I should have been doing a thousand other things and in the end, I had to see you to get rid of the feeling. I knew that someone as saintly as you would never do for me and I knew that as soon as I saw you the madness would go.'

He laughed quietly and hugged her to him and a happiness began to seep into her stiff and unhappy mind.

'My father had long since had the idea of a closer integration with the English firm we had acquired but I was not really interested. Now I pushed it hard and came to deal with it myself. You were out at lunch and when Bill glanced at your desk and said in an offhand manner that you were out, I realised that I had been holding my breath since I had met him. I had to wait and then you just walked right in. *Dio!* I thought I had been hit with a thunderbolt! I couldn't stop looking at you. And later, when you were so angry and showed the fight that I had expected to be so lacking in an angel, I knew that you were mine and nobody else was going to take you away.'

'You despatched Chris ruthlessly,' she murmured, her happiness beginning to grow as he stroked her hair.

'I am ruthless,' he confessed, tilting her face to kiss it, laughing into her eyes. 'He was not for you. I talked to him, listened to him. I am not saying that if he had been suitable for you I would have stepped aside, because I could not have done that, but he was so clearly in love with himself that Zarein seemed to be a very good idea, and he jumped at the chance to go and leave you. Since then,' he complained, 'you have given me hell. You walked deliberately into danger and you would never let me close enough to do anything to protect you. All I could do was house you where a little busybody would keep an eye on you.'

'Is that why you did it?' she asked, sitting up straight and looking at him properly for the first time.

'That and other reasons,' he confessed wryly. 'I wanted you, very badly. The arrangement seemed to be a good idea at that time.'

He saw the little burst of happiness leave her face and he pulled her tightly to him, kissing her suddenly pale cheeks.

'The night that Pearson put in his unexpected appearance,' he reminded her, 'you were more than willing to belong to me, to become the mistress that I had imagined I wanted, but at the last minute I looked at you and saw what I had not seen in my raging passion for you.' He looked deeply into her saddened eyes and smiled. 'I looked down at your face and I realised that I had been blinded for so long. I said to myself, "I love her!" Then I could not take you, even though my rejection hurt you, because you did not love me and it would not have been right.'

'I did love you!' she cried, happiness tearing through her unexpectedly at his confession. 'I loved you for long before that.'

'I did not know it until I saw the way you were when you thought I would crash,' he assured her softly. 'Then I knew, then it was beautiful and right. Oh, Rachel, you imagine that you will be ugly to me? Unwanted? The way I feel, knowing that you are carrying my child, is not possible to put into words. I am twenty feet tall! I am a giant! And you are mine!'

He pulled her tightly to him, his hands in the fiery glory of her hair, and kissed her until her bones threatened to melt and her breath was an unsteady gasp in her throat.

'We will get married in Rome,' he said with a definite finality, looking down at her as she lay against his shoulder, his eyes searching her every feature in a look of tender happiness that she had never before seen on his face.

'I haven't agreed to marry you,' she teased and he eyed her sternly, his hand grasping her chin.

'Your rights are severely restricted,' he warned her. 'In the first place you belong to me, and in the second place you have been putting that child of mine at risk in the hole that you ran to. You will not get far if you decide in one of your tempers to leave me after we are married, because then I will be able to get the item spread across the newspapers. "Nick Orsiani's wife missing! Great reward!" There would be no place to hide, my little wild cat. You would soon be brought back to me.'

'I'll never leave you, Nick!' she cried, her arms tightly round his neck. 'I'll trot along behind you wherever you go.'

'That would sound wonderful if I could believe it,' he laughed, 'but it does not sound in the least like you.'

'We could have our honeymoon here and then get married later,' she said dreamily, but he silenced that rather daring thought at once.

'No way! I'm not getting tricked into anything by a little red-headed witch. Tonight we stay here, tomorrow we fly to Rome and we announce our engagement at once. We will be married as soon as it can be arranged.'

'I'll have to see my mother,' Rachel said soberly after a while. 'I've phoned her, but I dared not tell her where I was. She'll be worried.'

'She will not have been the only one,' Nick stated fiercely. 'I have been growing old very rapidly worrying about you, and Toni and my father have been little help; naturally they have blamed me. I shall ring them both later. My father insisted upon leaving the telephone number of his hotel. Need I say that he is delighted to be able to have an angel in the family, poor unsuspecting man,' he added, laughing and catching her tightly against him when she objected to such insults.

'Your mother can come straight to Rome,' he said a few minutes later when her cheeks were burning from his kisses and her eyes were happily looking into his. 'She can stay in your flat and, if she likes, she can live there permanently. Perhaps the city will put a twinkle back into her eyes; perhaps even now she will find a happiness that will remove her bitterness. She will at the very least be able then to be near to her grandchild.'

'I never thought that I would be coming back.' Rachel sighed happily. 'I tossed a coin into the fountain but I thought it was only foolish, and now I'm going back to Rome after all.'

'And for ever,' he whispered, searching for her tender lips. 'Together we will plan our house on the hillside and when it is ready we will live there where we can look at the city at night when the children are asleep.'

She curled against him, her arms around his neck, and his hands found their way between the folds of the thick bathrobe, moving over her warm skin, caressing and loving, making her reach up to seek his lips.

'And speaking of children,' he murmured seductively, his hand warm on the still flat planes of her stomach, 'there is very little here to show for my efforts.'

She blushed wildly and then laughed up at him, happy as she had thought she would never be in her life.

'I've been biding my time,' she said with deliberate coquetry that made his hands tighten on her.

'So have I,' he confessed, his eyes darkening, 'but now I have run out of patience. Come to bed with me.'

'It's only the middle of the afternoon,' she protested as he stood and lifted her into his arms.

'We both need an early night,' he grinned. 'Anyone

can see that you need care and attention, and keeping my hands off you since I found you again has completely exhausted me.'

He stood her for a moment beside the big old-fashioned bed in the warm bedroom and looked down into her face, all his love there for her to see.

'Until we are too tired to kiss, too tired to touch each other, *cara*,' he said softly. 'Then we will sleep, but only for a little while.'

Her arms came tightly around him and they clung together in silence, the passion growing between them that had been there since their first meeting, and she wondered how she could ever have imagined another destiny. Love had removed the violence, the anger, from their passion and in its place was a warm and certain knowledge that they would never be apart again.

'You have never yet told me,' Nick said softly as he drew back to look with adoration into her radiant face. 'Not properly.'

'I love you, Nick,' she whispered happily. 'I love you, darling.'

And the joy on his face was all the reward she would ever need.

NOW ON VIDEO

Two great Romances available on video . . .*
from leading video retailers for just
£9·99
R.R.P.

The love you find in Dreams.

From Autumn 1987

YOU'RE INVITED TO ACCEPT **FOUR ROMANCES** AND A TOTE BAG **FREE!**

Acceptance card

| NO STAMP NEEDED | Post to: Reader Service, FREEPOST, P.O. Box 236, Croydon, Surrey. CR9 9EL |

Please note readers in Southern Africa write to:
Independant Book Services P.T.Y., Postbag X3010, Randburg 2125, S. Africa

YES! Please send me 4 free Mills & Boon Romances and my free tote bag – and reserve a Reader Service Subscription for me. If I decide to subscribe I shall receive 6 new Romances every month as soon as they come off the presses for £7.20 together with a FREE monthly newsletter including information on top authors and special offers, exclusively for Reader Service subscribers. There are no postage and packing charges, and I understand I may cancel or suspend my subscription at any time. If I decide not to subscribe I shall write to you within 10 days. Even if I decide not to subscribe the 4 free novels and the tote bag are mine to keep forever. I am over 18 years of age   EP20R

NAME _____

(CAPITALS PLEASE)

ADDRESS _____

_____

_____ POSTCODE _____

The right is reserved to refuse application and change the terms of this offer. You may be mailed with other offers as a result of this application. Offer expires March 31st 1988 and is limited to one per household.
Offer applies in UK and Eire only. Overseas send for details.

ROMANCE

Variety is the spice of romance

Each month, Mills & Boon publish new romances. New stories about people falling in love. A world of variety in romance — from the best writers in the romantic world. Choose from these titles in October.

A LATE LOVING Robyn Donald
THE POSITIVE APPROACH Emma Darcy
BLACK DIAMOND Joanna Mansell
SHADOW IN THE SUN Elizabeth Power
REBEL WITH A CAUSE Leigh Michaels
SECRET PASSION Carole Mortimer
QUICKSANDS Elizabeth Oldfield
UNFRIENDLY ALLIANCE Jessica Steele
LOST LAGOON Anne Weale
A MOMENT OF ANGER Patricia Wilson
*****GIFT BEYOND PRICE** Annabel Murray
*****DAUGHTER OF THE STARS** Quinn Wilder
*****BITTERSWEET PASSION** Lynne Graham
*****ROAD TO LOVE** Katherine Arthur

On sale where you buy paperbacks. If you require further information or have any difficulty obtaining them, write to: Mills & Boon Reader Service, PO Box 236, Thornton Road, Croydon, Surrey CR9 3RU, England.

*These four titles are available from Mills & Boon Reader Service.

Mills & Boon
the rose of romance

ROMANCE

Next month's romances from Mills & Boon

Each month, you can choose from a world of variety in romance with Mills & Boon. These are the new titles to look out for next month.

OUTSIDER Sara Craven
LEVELLING THE SCORE Penny Jordan
JUDGEMENT Madeleine Ker
OUT OF CONTROL Charlotte Lamb
LOVESCENES Sandra Marton
NO WINNER Daphne Clair
SAPPHIRE NIGHTS Valerie Parv
CAPTIVE LOVER Kate Walker
DESPERATE REMEDY Angela Wells
ULTIMATUM Sally Wentworth
*****SWEET PRETENCE** Jacqueline Gilbert
*****MARRY IN HASTE** Carol Gregor
*****EAGLE'S REVENGE** Liza Goodman
*****CRISPIN SUMMER** Sally Stewart

Buy them from your usual paperback stockist, or write to: Mills & Boon Reader Service, P.O. Box 236, Thornton Rd, Croydon, Surrey CR9 3RU, England. Readers in Southern Africa — write to: Independent Book Services Pty, Postbag X3010, Randburg, 2125, S. Africa.

*These four titles are available from Mills & Boon Reader Service.

Mills & Boon
the rose of romance

A BATTLE OF PASSION AND DENIAL

Freed from her tedious existence in England, Catrina sets sail for Gibraltar and her long lost family. She finds herself caught up in the tensions within the home and the onset of war with Spain.

Catrina falls hopelessly in love with the captain with the silvery eyes – the one man forbidden to her.

Can the secret of their illicit love remain hidden in an unforgiving society?

A colourful and stirring romance from Christina Laffeaty.

Available October Price £2.95

W●RLDWIDE

Available from Boots, Martins, John Menzies, W H Smith, Woolworths and other paperback stockists.